THE SHIPHANDLER'S GUIDE

for
Masters and Navigating Officers, Pilots and Tug Masters

Captain R.W. Rowe FNI

THE NAUTICAL INSTITUTE

THE SHIPHANDLER'S GUIDE

Published by The Nautical Institute
202 Lambeth Road, London SE1 7LQ, England
Telephone: +44 (0)207 928 1351
Fax: +44 (0)207 401 2817
Publications e-mail: pubs@nautinst.org
Worldwide web site: http://www.nautinst.org

First edition published 1996
Second edition published 2000
Second edition reprinted 2004
Copyright © The Nautical Institute, 2000

Photographs courtesy Howard Smith Towage and Salvage
and Warsash Maritime Centre

Typeset by Javafame Computer Services
90 Church Street, Lavenham, Suffolk CO10 9QT, England

Printed in England by
Modern Colour Solutions, Hayes Road, Southall, Middlesex UB2 5NB

ISBN 1 870077 35 0

THE SHIPHANDLER'S GUIDE

CONTENTS

LIST OF DIAGRAMS AND PHOTOGRAPHS

Figure	Description	Page

PHOTOGRAPHS

ACKNOWLEDGEMENTS

IT IS NOT THE INTENTION of this publication to make any attempt at explaining how a ship is berthed, or unberthed, at specific quays, docks and terminals. That is entirely the concern of the appropriately experienced personnel. The sole objective in each of the chapters of this 'Shiphandler's Guide' is to discuss how a ship behaves under certain circumstances or conditions and to highlight any difficulties that might be encountered, as an aid to ship handling anywhere in the world.

In the light of many years of experience in the use of ship simulators and manned models, as an aid for training personnel in ship handling, it has been proved many times over that it is absolutely essential to strike a critical balance between theoretical content and practical application. With this experience in mind, it has been the deliberate intention throughout this publication to reduce the complex mathematical data of the academic world of ship handling to the very simplest level possible, so that it might be understood more easily and applied to the practical world afloat.

It is hoped that this practical 'Guide' will give all personnel involved in the handling of ships a working knowledge of how a ship behaves, so that in the future they can come to their own conclusions with respect to a particular manoeuvre, in terms of its feasibility or difficulties. This may, for example, be particularly useful to masters taking command for the first time after a long period as chief officer, and to new pilots during the tripping stage of their training period. It might also prove a useful reference book and aid for more experienced personnel, when they are endeavouring to analyse a specific manoeuvre, incident or casualty.

I would particularly like to thank my working colleagues at the Warsash Maritime Centre for their support in this project and Captain M.C. Banbury, FNI, Managing Director of Howard Smith Towage, London, Dr. Ian Dand of British Maritime Technology and Captain P.J.D. Russell, FNI, London Pilot, for reading the text and for their constructive comments.

I would like to acknowledge and thank the many pilots and ship masters around the world, that I have worked with over the years, all of whom in some way or another have contributed towards this work. I dedicate this publication to them.

The Author

PREFACE

Captain George Angas, ExC, FNI
The Director — Warsash Maritime Centre

THE CHALLENGES THAT FACE the international maritime transport industry can only be resolved on an international scale. From which it follows that no one element of the industry can succeed without a good understanding and close co-operation with other elements from within the same industry. In order to maintain and enhance seafarer standards a good working relationship must exist between the seafarers themselves, their employers, professional maritime bodies and maritime training centres throughout the world. This book has been developed and written on this basis, e.g. the author, a skilled and experienced mariner working within a proactive maritime training and education centre, providing courses and consultancy for shipping companies and pilots from around the world for many years, has now placed on paper some of that knowledge and experience for the benefit of existing and future mariners.

This has been a well understood and active process over many years. What is different now, however, is that the level of relationship between these parts of our multifaceted industry has changed. Whereas in the not too distant past maritime colleges were seen more as ivory towers providing education and training to fixed national norms, we are now working hard with shipowners and operators to develop a relationship in which we are seen as an extension of their own operation which can make a meaningful contribution to the success of a commercial venture. Maritime colleges themselves cannot solely rely on state funding for their existence and must provide a proactive contribution to ensure that ship operators can maintain their operating costs to a minimum by effective training and assessment of the crews that man their ships.

The Warsash Maritime Centre, near Southampton in England, is proud to be able to contribute to our industry, not only in direct training and education but also through dissemination of knowledge and experience in books such as this. It is publications such as these that also demonstrate the close working relationship between maritime education and training establishments and the professional bodies. The Nautical Institute, for example, is facilitating the dissemination of knowledge by providing very effective publications that reach all parts of the world. We hope that you, the reader of this book, will obtain both pleasure and knowledge from it and that it will be a valuable contribution to the development of your skill as one of the world's seafarers.

FOREWORD 1

Captain E.H. Beetham, FNI
Past President, The Nautical Institute

IT IS A JOY TO LOOK AT A BOOK on ship handling that presents the behaviour of ships in such a practical way. "Why" we may ask ourselves "was it not presented in this way before?"

I think the answer lies in the lasting influence of the traditional approach that does not always meet the needs of todays mariners. In the days of sail, when certificates of competency were introduced, there was instruction and examination on how to avoid dangerous situations and how to turn wind, tide and weather to best advantage.

Those who sat their certificates in more recent times demonstrated their ship handling ability with wooden models. Text books illustrated standard situations with the plan view of a pram dinghy. No damage was suffered by either ships or quays and shallow water effects were notably absent.

Having been trained to handle models the officer was not introduced to the geometry of a turning ship, the changing pivot point or the hydrodynamic influences that can make the end result so different to the intended manoeuvre. We were not trained to control a moving ship in a confined area.

The Royal Navy, by contrast, had a practical solution to the problem by making sure that midshipmen under training handled the cutters, pinnaces and rescue boats which gave them both the feel and responsibility at an early stage.

The great worry for the future is that the industry and the armed services will claim that it is too expensive to provide practical training in shiphandling. It is expensive, time consuming but necessary. The greatest benefit of this book is that it lays the right foundation for understanding the science of the individual factors that combine to create the art of shiphandling.

One proposed solution to ship handling training is to use simulators — which are extensively used in the aviation industry for pilot training — but while valuable for the seaman, they rely on visual response to change. The strength of this approach is that they can be used to familiarise the ship handler with varied situations in a safe environment but the weakness of simulation is the absence of a sense of movement that makes it difficult to appreciate the interactive forces. Simulator time, costs and availability will inevitably restrict the extent of training that is possible.

The scale models used at Marchwood and Grenoble are probably the most practical way of attempting different manoeuvres and of learning the basic principles. The quality of model and simulator training relies on the dedication of the staff and the author comes from the worthy group who run the ship handling courses at the Warsash Maritime Centre.

This book will supplement any simulator training and will provide guidance for a master whose ship has to perform an unfamiliar manoeuvre. It will give much easy reading to allow those in control of ships to anticipate events and to gain an awareness of why the ship responds in different ways and what influences those responses.

I hope this book becomes a standard text for all those who aspire to control or command a ship at sea. I think it will be of immense value to them.

FOREWORD 2

Captain P.J.D. Russell, FNI, London Pilot
President, The Nautical Institute

As A PILOT with some 30 years personal experience of ship handling it gives me great pleasure to contribute a foreword to this excellent training manual. The training of pilots is frequently under scrutiny. No doubt there will be much written by those who have never had responsibility for the safe navigation of a ship to or from a berth as to exactly how it should be done. Their views will be regarded with some scepticism. The first thing most pilots will do is to go to the author's curriculum vitae to read exactly who is trying to teach them how to do their job and whether or not the author has the necessary experience, in their view, to teach them anything. That is an unfortunate fact of life. It was, in fact, my first reaction when asked to look at the manuscript and I did not find the kind of actual ship handling experience there for which a pilot might be looking. I therefore started to read the manuscript with some considerable scepticism.

I very soon realised that this book was something special. I became impressed with the clarity of presentation and the value of the information collated for all pilots and those charged with the safe manoeuvring of ships. I have, over the years, studied many books on ship handling and suggest that this book is, without doubt, one of the best I have come across.

Pilots remain, I know, of the opinion that the very best training they can receive is on the bridge of a ship under the supervision of an experienced pilot. That system, however, does have a couple of weaknesses that this book can help to alleviate. The first weakness is that some of the very best pilots may be a joy to watch in action but may not necessarily be good teachers. The second weakness is that there are still many pilots around who look upon ship handling as some kind of 'art' whereby they instinctively respond and react from experience to the movement of the ship. They may, in fact, go through a highly successful career doing just that, rather than fully understanding the science behind those reactions and reasons for their need. This book will not only help them better to understand their 'art' but perhaps avoid some of the more dramatic responses by allowing them to be proactive instead of reactive. The Shiphandler's Guide will also enable them to become better at passing on relevant information to the next generation.

I congratulate Bob Rowe on his thoughtful work and have no hesitation in commending this book to anyone with an interest in ship handling.

Shiphandling with tug assistance

CHAPTER ONE

GENERAL AND INTRODUCTION TO THE PIVOT POINT

General

THE SKILL OF A GOOD SHIPHANDLER should never be underestimated. This is because they can achieve consistency in performance and control even though no two dockings are ever exactly the same. Similarly the range of variable considerations which have to be taken into account when planning, predicting, monitoring and manoeuvring means the shiphandler is constantly having to reassess progress.

The competent shiphandler has to be aware of wind and weather, current and tidal changes. In most berth approaches, shallow water and interaction effects will also have to be taken into account.

There is the range, type, availability and efficiency of tugs to be considered. Also, the availability and aptitude of the personnel on each ship has to be assessed for their ability to handle tow lines and mooring lines. All these factors effect ship manoeuvres which in a tidal regime have to be completed within limited time windows: so adding to the sense of anxiety should anything go wrong.

We can start to see that the qualities demanded of a good shiphandler are considerably greater than those required in other modes of transport. They must be competent in the sense that they are trained and know what they intend to achieve. They must be able to exercise judgement and be flexible in their outlook to adjust to changing circumstances. They must be able to communicate effectively; they must be able to stay calm under pressure and solve problems with authority when the situation requires it, and they have to be experienced.

Shiphandling is teamwork and for teamwork to be successful there has to be a general understanding amongst pilots, masters, tug masters, ships officers and dock masters about the principles of shiphandling and the factors which influence manoeuvring.

In a perceptive article by Julian Parker, Secretary of The Nautical Institute, he pointed out that words and sentences flow in a sequence, whereas the need in shiphandling is to have an awareness of the whole picture during manoeuvres. It is one of the reasons I believe, why it is so difficult to convey the essence of shiphandling in a written text.

My approach to this book has been different. Each situation is based upon a diagram which contains the essential information for visualising the particular point being made. I have then added the text to explain in more detail how the forces represented in a static diagram interact when the ship is moving or being manoeuvred.

As I indicated earlier there is much more to ship handling than a book can convey. For this reason I do not think it is appropriate to try and describe how to approach berths in specific ports or how to plan a particular estuarial passage. That level of detail must remain the responsibility of the senior pilots who best know the local areas and provide the detailed training necessary.

I do however, believe that by having a clearly prepared set of diagrams to illustrate the key factors in shiphandling readers will come to have a better understanding of the principles involved.

These principles are based upon a number of moving influences some internal like thrust and the position of the pivot point, some external like wind and interaction. It is these moving variable forces that have to be mastered and the first place to start is the pivot point.

The Pivot Point

Ship Stopped
Fig. 1(a)

Unless stated otherwise, each example assumes a ship on even keel, in calm conditions and still water. In this situation no forces are involved and the ship has a pivot point coinciding with its centre of gravity, approximately amidships.

Making Headway
Fig. 1(b)

Two forces now come into play. Firstly, the forward momentum of the ship and secondly, longitudinal resistance to the forward momentum, created by the water ahead of the ship. These two forces must ultimately strike a balance and the pivot point moves forward. As a rough guide it can be assumed that at a steady speed the pivot point will be approximately 25% or a $1/4$ of the ship's length from forward.

Making Sternway
Fig. 1(c)

The situation is now totally reversed. The momentum of sternway must balance longitudinal resistance, this time created by the water astern of the ship. The pivot point now moves aft and establishes itself approximately 25% or a $1/4$ of the ship's length from the stern.

Although not intended, some publications may give the impression that the pivot point moves right aft with sternway. This is clearly not correct and can sometimes be misleading. It should also be stressed that other factors such as acceleration, shape of hull and speed may all affect the position of the pivot point. The arbitrary figures quoted here, however, are perfectly adequate for a simple and practical working knowledge of the subject.

Turning Levers

More important, perhaps, than the position of the pivot point, is the effect its shifting nature has upon the many turning forces that can influence a ship. These are — rudder force, transverse thrust, bow thrust, tug force, interactive forces and the forces of wind and tide.

Vessel Stopped
Fig. 2(a)

If we look at the ship used in our example, we can see that it has a length overall of 160 metres. It is stopped in the water and two tugs are secured fore and aft, on long lines, through centre leads. If the tugs apply the same bollard pull of, say, 15 tonnes (t) each, it is to a position 80m fore and aft of the pivot point. Thus two equal turning levers and moments of 80m x 15t (1200tm) are created resulting in even lateral motion and no rate of turn.

Making Headway
Fig. 2(b)

With the ship making steady headway, however, the pivot point has shifted to a position 40m from the bow. The forward tug is now working on a very poor turning lever of 40m x 15t (600tm), whilst the after tug is working on an extremely good turning lever of 120m x 15t (1800tm). This results in a swing of the stern to port.

Making Sternway
Fig. 2(c)

The efficiency of the tugs will change totally when, by contrast, the ship makes sternway. Now the pivot point has moved aft to a position 40m from the stern. The forward tug is working on an excellent turning lever of 120m x 15t (1800tm) whilst the after tug has lost its efficiency to a reduced turning lever of 40m x 15t (600tm). This now results in a swing of the bow to port.

Fig. 1 The Pivot Point

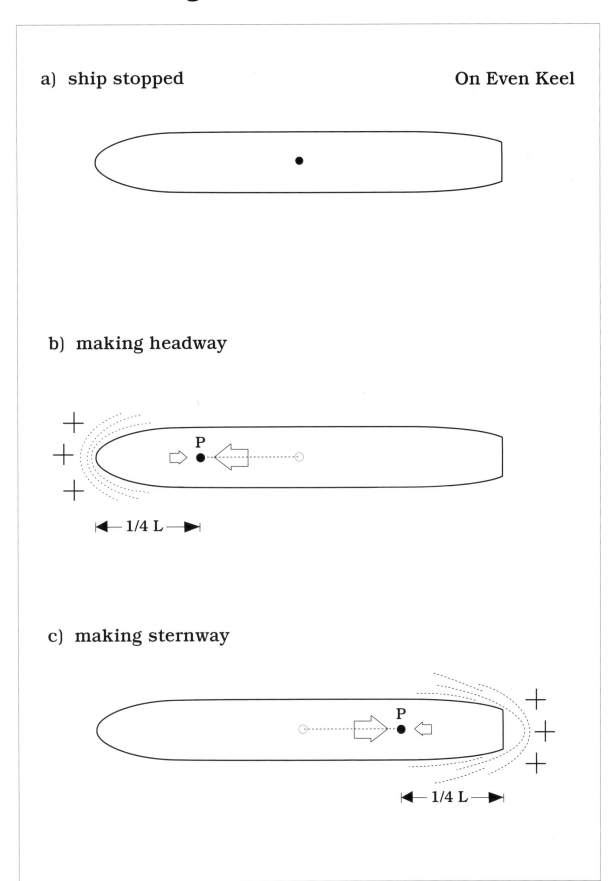

a) ship stopped   On Even Keel

b) making headway

P

← 1/4 L →

c) making sternway

P

← 1/4 L →

Fig. 2 Turning Levers and Moments

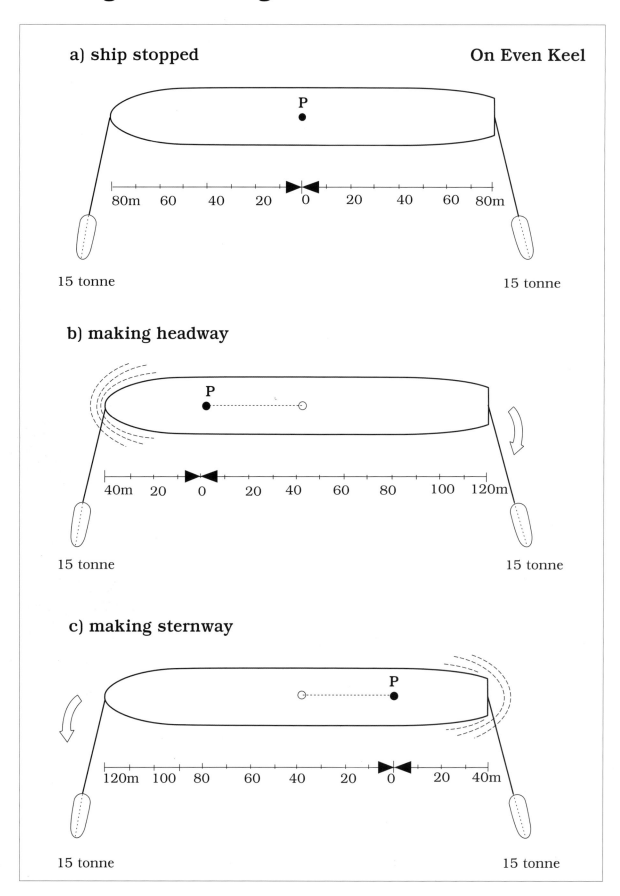

a) ship stopped

On Even Keel

P

80m 60 40 20 0 20 40 60 80m

15 tonne

15 tonne

b) making headway

P

40m 20 0 20 40 60 80 100 120m

15 tonne

15 tonne

c) making sternway

P

120m 100 80 60 40 20 0 20 40m

15 tonne

15 tonne

Summary

This simple method can also be used as an aid to understanding many practical aspects of shiphandling such as rudder, propeller and thruster efficiency, the effect of wind, trim, interaction and tug positioning. In each of the following chapters which discusses these particular subject areas it is a useful basis from which to start!

Note

The full hull form of the average merchant ship is used throughout this guide in terms of length to breadth ratio and general profile.

The guide does not cover unusual circumstances which may be experienced when considering less common vessels such as fine lined, high speed warships, non displacement craft and vessels with exceptional profiles.

Shiphandling in locks and basins requires special skills

CHAPTER TWO

SLOW SPEED CONTROL

General

THE ESTIMATION OF SPEED and knowing when to reduce speed when approaching a berth is not always easy. Confidence can only come with experience. On very large ships, such as VLCCs, some guidance may be available from reliable doppler logs, but on many ships a doppler log is not available. In any case, total reliance upon instrumentation is not wise and is no substitute for experience. A pilot jumping from one ship to another, sometimes several during one duty period, has to develop a 'feel' for the type of ship he boards and drive it 'by the seat of his pants'.

Speed

Many casualties are proven to occur as a direct result of excessive speed. Its effect can be insidious and a master may find that it is difficult to keep up with events which are happening too quickly. Effective control of the ship can be slowly but inexorably lost. Against this are commercial pressures, on masters and pilots alike, for expedient passages and turn-round times. Whilst there are arguments either way, they are clearly not compatible and experience has shown that a fast pilot is not necessarily a good pilot — just a lucky one!

It is therefore desirable to balance a safe and effective speed of approach against a realistic time scale. It would be unwise, for example, to conduct a three mile run-in at a speed of one knot. Three hours would stretch anyone's patience!

It is, of course, impossible to give exact figures. The requirement is dictated to a large degree by variable factors such as type of ship, tonnage, draft, shaft horsepower, wind and tide. Generally speaking, ships of less than 40,000 dwt, for example, are inclined to run their way off relatively quickly when engine speed is reduced, whereas larger ships carry their way for much larger distances and their speed must be brought firmly under control at greater distances from the berth.

It is usually obvious when the speed of a ship is too slow, and can easily be overcome with a small increase in revolutions. It is not always obvious, though, when the speed is too high. The speed of a large ship during an approach to a berth, particularly without tugs, can increase in an insidious manner. It is invariably difficult to reduce that speed in a short distance and keep control of the ship.

Loss of Control
Fig. 3

If we look at figure 3 we can illustrate some important points. In this example we have a medium size ship of 60,000 dwt, which we will assume is diesel powered, with a single, right handed, fixed pitch propeller and a single conventional rudder.

At one mile from the berth, running at an approach speed of 6 knots, it is well in excess of the ship's dead slow speed of 3 knots. As the ship approaches the 1/2 mile mark, speed is still over 3 knots, despite a rapid reduction in rpm. It is now necessary to stop the engine

Fig. 3 — Loss of Slow Speed Control

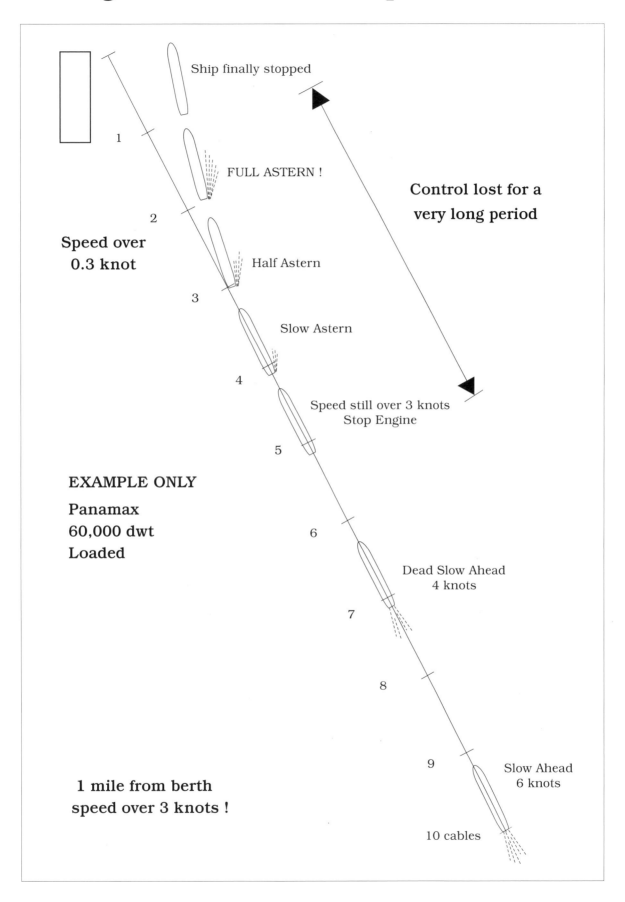

Ship finally stopped

1

FULL ASTERN !

2

Speed over
0.3 knot

Half Astern

3

Slow Astern

Control lost for a
very long period

4

Speed still over 3 knots
Stop Engine

5

EXAMPLE ONLY

Panamax
60,000 dwt
Loaded

6

Dead Slow Ahead
4 knots

7

8

9

Slow Ahead
6 knots

1 mile from berth
speed over 3 knots !

10 cables

and thence sustain a prolonged period of increasing stern power, in order to stop the ship in time. During this substantial time interval, the ship is at the whim of transverse thrust, wind, tide and bank or shallow water effect. It is effectively 'out of control' in so much that we can only stand back and hope that it will do what is required. This is literally a hit or miss situation and the more we can reduce this prolonged period of increasing stern power and thus retain control, so much the better!

Slow Speed Control
Fig. 4

In figure 4 we see the same ship, again one mile from a berth but this time at its dead slow speed of 3 knots or less. Before it approaches the $1/2$ mile mark it may also be necessary to stop the engine to further reduce the headway and allow plenty of time for adjusting the ship's approach and positioning for the berth.

One of the biggest worries is the loss of rudder effectiveness and the fear that we cannot keep control of the ship's head at very slow speeds, particularly without any tug assistance. For a variety of reasons such as poor steering, wind, tide, shallow water or directional instability, the bow may well begin to develop an unwanted sheer, also it may be desirable to adjust the attitude of approach. Control is best achieved by applying full rudder and utilising a short but substantial burst of engine power. **This is the 'kick ahead' technique**.

There are however, several pitfalls to avoid, which can all lead to an excessive increase in speed, thus ruining all the previous efforts to control it.

Kick Ahead — Rudder Angle

If a kick ahead is to be utilised, it is essential that the rudder is seen to be 'hard over' before the power is applied. Whilst this ensures a maximum rudder turning force, it also 'puts the brake on' some of the residual speed, directly resulting from increased power. With the helm at anything less, such as 15° or 20°, less rudder force is applied at the cost of increasing forward speed. It is also essential that the power is taken off before the rudder is returned to amidships or to angles of less than 35°. Failure to do this will result in a brief, but important interval, during which time most or all of the power applied, is again being used to increase speed.

Kick Ahead — Duration

The duration of a kick ahead should be as short as possible. Prolonged use of the power, after the initial steering effect has ceased, will only result in a violent sheer and an unwanted build up of speed. This will result in the need for yet another kick ahead to rectify the situation. As soon as the revolutions reach the required maximum, the power must be taken off.

Kick Ahead — Power
Fig. 5

It is difficult to quantify the amount of power to apply for a kick ahead, as it very much depends on the size of ship and the needs of the ship handler at the time. It is important, however, to appreciate the ratio of shaft horse power (shp) to tonnage (dwt) that exists from ship to ship.

If we look at a table of new tonnages from a Japanese ship yard, (see figure 5) there are enormous differences with increasing ship size. The cargo ship of 20,000 dwt

Fig. 4 — Maintaining Slow Speed Control

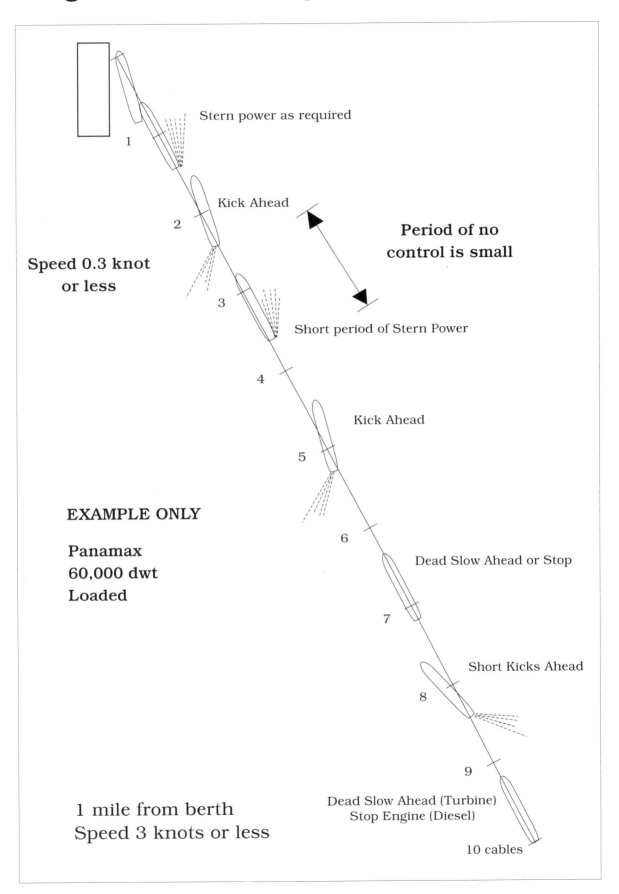

Stern power as required

Kick Ahead

Period of no control is small

Short period of Stern Power

Speed 0.3 knot or less

Kick Ahead

EXAMPLE ONLY

Panamax
60,000 dwt
Loaded

Dead Slow Ahead or Stop

Short Kicks Ahead

Dead Slow Ahead (Turbine)
Stop Engine (Diesel)

1 mile from berth
Speed 3 knots or less

10 cables

Fig. 5 Shaft/Brake Horse Power *

SHIP TYPE	DWT Tonnes	LBP	B	DRAFT	ENGINE	SHP
Tankers	380,000	355	64	23	Turbine	45,000
	250,000	320	52	21	Turbine	31,000
Tankers	120,000	252	38	17	Diesel	23,000
	100,000	251	38	15	Diesel	21,000
	80,000	237	36	12	Diesel	20,000
	60,000	219	32	12	Diesel	15,000
Bulk Cargo	190,000	285	50	18	Diesel	24,000
	120,000	248	38	18	Diesel	23,000
	80,000	237	36	12	Diesel	17,000
	60,000	218	32	12	Diesel	15,000
	30,000	163	24	11	Diesel	13,000
	20,000	146	22	9	Diesel	9,000
Cargo	20,000	157	26	10	Diesel	17,000
	12,000	146	22	10	Diesel	11,000
Car Carrier	12,500	180	32	9	Diesel	10,400
Container (23 knots)						
TEU 1940	29,000	196	32	11	Diesel	26,200
TEU 839	23,000	213	30	9	Diesel	30,000

LBP = Length between perpendiculars: metres
B = Maximum breadth: metres
SHP = Shaft Horse Power

* Shaft horse power (shp) is that generated to turn the propeller. It is almost equivalent to brake horse power (bhp) which is the actual power developed by the engine. For shiphandling purposes they can be assumed to be the same.

has a substantial 17,000 shp; the tanker of 60,000 dwt, by contrast, has only 15,000 shp. The VLCC of 250,000 dwt, which is four times larger than the tanker, has only twice the engine power at 31,000 shp.

In practical terms, a kick ahead with slow ahead may be very effective on a smaller ship, but extremely inadequate for a VLCC, when half or even full power may be needed to achieve any result. This does not, of course, encompass that peculiar breed of ship which for some reason are built with speeds of 6 or 8 knots at dead slow ahead! In this case a 'kick ahead' at dead slow will be advisable.

Type of propulsion unit

The type of propulsion unit is also an important factor to consider when utilising the kick ahead. Diesel-powered ships are generally very good, with the power coming in quickly and effectively. The number of engine air starts, however, varies considerably from ship to ship. Some may be good and have an unlimited start-up capacity, others may have only two air bottles which at very best might give 10 to 12 starts each. Far worse cases can be experienced, with the infamous words "only one start left pilot" ruining what was otherwise a good day! Fortunately only a few of these ships are around today.

Working with a turbine ship is very different, in so much as a turbine is slow to come on line and build up power. This is not particularly useful for kicks ahead. When slowing down, but still wishing to keep control of heading, it is better, if it is permissible, to leave the turbine on dead slow for as long as possible rather than stop the engine. The turbine is thus on line and instantly available for use.

Summary

Without the assistance of tugs to control both heading and speed, the correct use of the kick ahead is the single most effective means of keeping control of heading and speed, particularly with directionally unstable ships. Clearly the ship must be stopped at sometime and indeed several kicks ahead, no matter how carefully applied, will result in a slow build up of speed. This can be carefully balanced, with short periods of modest stern power, thereby just easing the speed back, or even stopping the ship entirely if so desired.

The master or pilot is thus able to enjoy far longer periods of total control and this would not be possible with the ship running at too high a speed.

Car carriers present a particular problem when operating in windy conditions

Manned models are ideal for training in shiphandling, particularly slow speed control without tug assistance

CHAPTER THREE

TRANSVERSE THRUST

Ahead Movement of the Propeller

THE EFFECT OF TRANSVERSE THRUST whilst making an ahead movement is arguably less worrying than that of an astern movement, perhaps because the result is less noticeable. Propeller design is a complex subject area, but it is worth looking at the main factors, which are evident with an ahead movement of a right handed propeller.

- The helical discharge from the propeller creates a larger pressure on the port side of the rudder.

- A slight upward flow from the hull into the propeller area puts slightly more pressure onto the down sweeping propeller blades.

- It is evident during tests that the speed or flow of water into a propeller area is uneven in velocity.

The net result is a tendency for a right handed propeller to give a small swing to port when running ahead. Whilst this may be noticeable in calm and near perfect conditions it is easily influenced by other likely factors such as wind, current, shallow water, tugs, rudder errors and so on.

Astern Movement of the Propeller

The importance of transverse thrust when using an astern movement, is of much greater significance to the ship handler. The helical discharge, or flow, from a right handed propeller working astern splits and passes forward towards either side of the hull. In doing so it behaves quite differently. On the port quarter it is inclined down and away from the hull whilst on the starboard quarter it is directed up and on to the hull. This flow of water striking the starboard quarter can be a substantial force in tonnes that is capable of swinging the stern to port giving the classic '**kick round**' or '**cut**' of the bow to starboard.

Force in Tonnes

Mainly a function of water flow, transverse thrust can be increased or decreased by varying propeller rpm. This in turn varies the magnitude of the force in tonnes applied to the quarter and it can be viewed clinically, as one of the forces available to the ship handler, in much the same manner as rudder, tug or bow thruster forces. It is, however, a weak force and can be roughly calculated if the shp of a particular ship is known.

For example let us take a ship of 80,000 dwt with a full ahead of 20,000 shp. If full astern is only 50% of this then it only has a maximum of 10,000 shp astern. For practical purposes it can be taken as a rough guide that transverse thrust is only 5 to 10% of the applied stern power. Therefore, in this case, a force of 1,000 shp or 10 tonnes at best (assuming 100 shp = 1 tonne).

Whilst shaft horsepower is an important factor in determining the magnitude of transverse thrust and how much a ship will cut when going astern, a further consideration must be the position of the pivot point.

Pivot Point and Transverse Thrust

Vessel Making Headway
Fig. 6(a)

Consider another ship, this time of 26,000 dwt with a maximum of 6,000 shp astern (see figure 6a). It can be seen that shp relates to approximately 6 tonnes of force on the starboard quarter. When the ship is making slow enough headway for the propeller wash to reach the hull, it is acting upon a pivot point that is forward and thus a turning lever of 110 metres. This creates a substantial turning moment of 660 tonne-metres.

The forward speed of the ship must be considered, because at higher speeds the full force of propeller wash will not be striking the quarter. As the ship progressively comes down to lower speeds and with the pivot point still forward, the magnitude of transverse thrust will slowly increase reaching its peak just prior to the ship being completely stopped. It is an unfortunate fact of life that at the slower speeds approaching a berth, if stern power is applied, transverse thrust is likely to be at its maximum!

Vessel Making Sternway
Fig. 6(b)

With the same ship making sternway the pivot point will now move to a new position somewhere aft of amidships (see figure 6b). With the propeller working astern the flow of water on to the starboard quarter is still maintaining its magnitude as a force of 6 tonnes but is now applied to a reduced turning lever of 40 metres.

Unlike the situation with headway we now have a reduced turning moment of 240 tonne-metres with sternway. In the first instance this may not seem strikingly important. It must be remembered, however, that transverse thrust may be a poor force in comparison to other forces such as wind and tide. With the example of sternway, a wind acting forward of the pivot point may be strong enough to overcome that of transverse thrust. This will be investigated more thoroughly in later chapters concerning the effects of wind and tide.

It is sometimes apparent that a ship when using stern power in the close proximity of solid jetties, banks or shallow water will 'cut' the wrong way. There are two possible causes for this occurrence and only a pilot's local knowledge is likely to pinpoint them.

Anomalies

Wedge Effect
Fig. 6(b)

The first is a phenomenon known as '**wedge effect**'. This occurs when the ship with a fixed pitch right handed propeller has a solid jetty or other vertical obstruction close to its starboard side. If excessive stern power is used, the wash created is forced forward between the ship and the obstruction. If we again look at figure 6b, it can be seen that if the flow of water is restricted then a force is exerted on the ship forward of the pivot point.

This is particularly apparent when the ship is stopped or making sternway. The force may be of sufficient strength to kill normal transverse thrust and sometimes generate a swing of the bow to port. It will be worse if the ship has a bow-in aspect or is land locked forward of the berth, thus increasing the entrapment of water flow. Whilst a disadvantage in some respects it can be turned to advantage in some parts of the world. Using the 'wedge effect', a ship can be lifted bodily off a solid jetty when backing out, to avoid dragging the bow along the dock side.

Fig. 6 Transverse Thrust with Stern Power

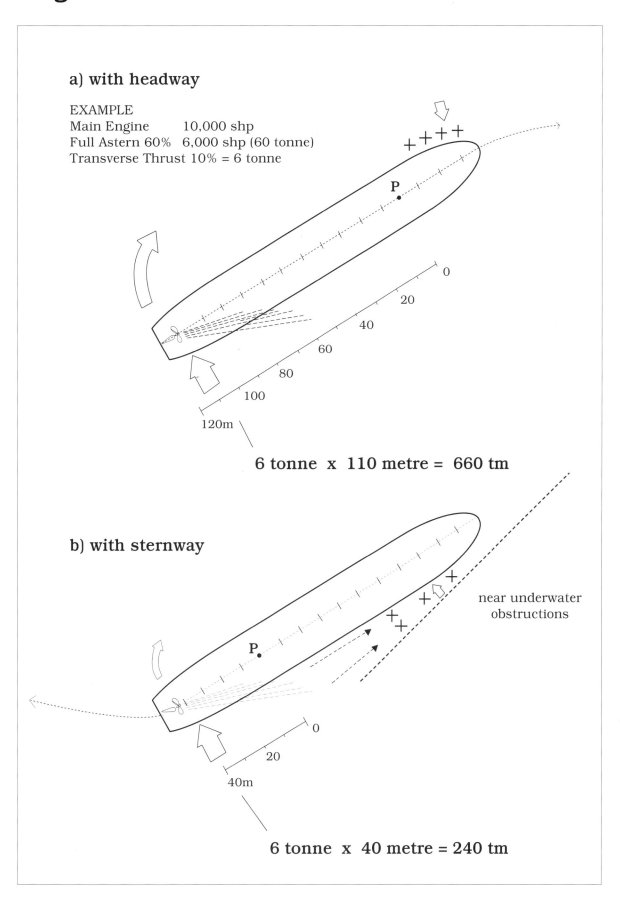

a) with headway

EXAMPLE
Main Engine   10,000 shp
Full Astern 60%   6,000 shp (60 tonne)
Transverse Thrust 10% = 6 tonne

P.

0
20
40
60
80
100
120m

6 tonne x 110 metre = 660 tm

b) with sternway

P.

near underwater
obstructions

0
20
40m

6 tonne x 40 metre = 240 tm

Effect of Shallow Water

The second possible cause of a 'cut' the wrong way may be attributed to the vicinity of shallow water. The flow of water from the fixed pitch right handed propeller working astern as we have seen, is up and on to the starboard quarter, but down and away from the port quarter. If the ship has a small under keel clearance it is possible that, in addition to such factors as cavitation and restricted flow into the propeller, the flow of water on the port side is being deflected off the bottom and back on to the hull. This clearly gives some prior indication that the response of the ship may be unpredictable in shallow water and, once again, the bow may swing the wrong way.

Throughout these examples we have, for practical purposes, adopted a simplistic approach by only considering a fixed pitch right handed propeller. There are of course ships with fixed pitch left handed propellers, propeller tunnels and controllable pitch propellers, the latter becoming increasingly more common.

Alternative Design Features
Left Handed Propeller

With a left handed propeller it is simply a case of remembering that the results of transverse thrust are the opposite in so much that the flow of water from the propeller working astern is up and on to the port quarter and not the starboard quarter. In basic terms the 'cut' of the bow is therefore to port when working the propeller astern.

Controllable Pitch Propeller

The controllable pitch propeller rotates constantly in the same direction no matter what movement is demanded of it. Viewed from astern, a clockwise rotating propeller is still rotating clockwise with stern power, only the pitch angle of the blades has changed. This gives the same effect as a conventional fixed pitch left handed propeller, which is also rotating clockwise when going astern, the bow will swing to port. Similarly if a variable pitch propeller constantly rotates counter clockwise when viewed from astern, this will be the same as a fixed pitch right handed propeller which is also rotating counter clockwise during an astern movement, the bow will thus swing to starboard.

Shrouds

For economical purposes, propellers in shrouds or tunnels are growing in number, even on large VLCCs. This ultimately has some bearing upon transverse thrust because they alter significantly the flow of water exiting the propeller area. It may be more concentrated and is likely to impose an equal thrust upon both sides of the hull thus resulting in little or no transverse thrust.

Hull Design

Finally, hull design features may also play a significant part in altering this simplistic and traditional concept of transverse thrust. It is possible, for example, because of a different hull shape or length to breadth ratio, for the point of impact of water flow to be much closer to the position of the pivot point when backing. In such a case, transverse thrust, although relatively pronounced with headway, may be surprisingly weak with sternway, to the extent that the bow may literally fall off either way, particularly if influenced by wind or shallow water.

Some of these subject areas will be discussed in more detail in later chapters of this publication.

CHAPTER FOUR

TURNING

General

IT IS QUITE CLEAR from the results of numerous casualty investigations that a failure to turn a ship in the available sea room ranks high amongst the causes of many accidents, some literally terminal. This can be for a number of reasons such as mechanical failure, human error or adverse weather conditions. **In the category of human error, excessive speed whilst attempting to turn is once again a major source of failure**.

Rudder Force and Pivot Point
Fig. 7

We will start with a ship of 26,000 tonne displacement, stopped dead in the water assuming even keel, calm conditions and no tide (see figure 7). With the rudder hard to starboard, an ahead movement is now applied and for the moment it is academic whether it is dead slow, slow, half or full. This we can refer to simply as '**1. Rudder Force**'. This will be attempting to both turn the ship and drive it forward. Forward movement is initially resisted because of the inertia of the ship, whilst the turn, which is working at the end of the ship on a good lever, sets in slightly earlier. This results in a pivot point which is initially well forward and approximately $^1/_8$ L (P) from the bow. The importance of this is absolutely vital because at this stage, with the ship just beginning to make headway and the pivot point well forward, we have the optimum rudder force. It will never be better!

Thereafter, when the ship begins to build up speed, the water resistance ahead of the ship balances forward power and pushes the pivot point back a further $^1/_4$ L (see chapter 1). At a steady speed, whilst turning, the final position of the pivot point will now be approximately $^1/_3$ L (PP) from the bow. With the turning lever thus reduced the rudder force has now become progressively less efficient.

Lateral Resistance

As a ship commences to turn and thereafter for the duration of a turn, the ship is sliding sideways through the water. This results in a large build up of water resistance, all the way down the ship's side, which continually opposes the rudder force and which we can refer to as the '**2. Lateral Resistance**'. The balance between the rudder force and the lateral resistance, plays a crucial part in shaping all turning circles.

Constant RPM Turns
Fig. 8 and 9

If, for example, our ship of 26,000 tonne displacement enters and continues a turn at a constant rpm for slow ahead, both forces balance to give a turning circle as shown in figure 8. The advance and transfer can be measured from the scale for both 20° and 35° turns. By comparison, looking at the same ship, conducting a turn at a constant rpm for full ahead in figure 9, it may be surprising to note that the turning circles are virtually identical to the slow ahead turns.

The reasons for this are due to the fact that although we have entered the turn with a much larger rudder force, it is also with a higher speed and therefore higher lateral resistance. In any turn at constant rpm, rudder force and

Fig. 7 Lateral Forces when Turning

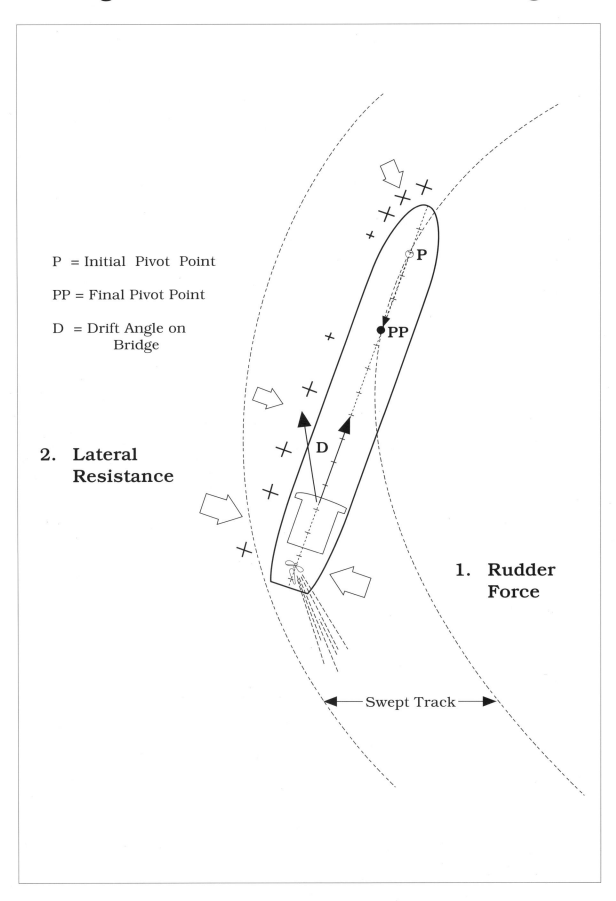

P = Initial Pivot Point

PP = Final Pivot Point

D = Drift Angle on Bridge

2. Lateral Resistance

1. Rudder Force

Swept Track

lateral resistance are always achieving the same balance thereby assuring that each turning circle is approximately the same, in terms of advance and transfer. The only thing that is saved by entering a turn at higher speeds is time. It is the 'rate of turn' which varies. Whilst this can be critical in cases when time is of paramount importance, such as conducting a large turn across a strong tide or taking the ship through a 'Williamson Turn', it does not improve turning ability.

Speed during a Turn
Fig. 9

The speed of a ship during a normal turn is interesting, in so much that it suffers a marked reduction. As the ship is sliding sideways and ahead, the exposed side experiences a substantial increase in water resistance, which in turn acts as a brake. The ship may experience a 30 to 50% speed loss and it is a useful feature in many areas of ship handling where a sharp speed reduction is required. The ship in figure 9, for example, entered the turn at a full speed of 11 6 knots. Once it has settled into the turn, the speed will be reduced to about 6 to 8 knots. This is useful in a Williamson Turn, allowing it in the interests of time to be conducted at full speed, yet knowing that the turn alone will take a great deal of the speed off. Similarly many pilots will come up to a single buoy mooring (SBM) with one and sometimes two 90° turns in the approach, as this will ensure that the speed is brought down. In short, it is a useful and very effective method of speed reduction, with which to fall back on, should it be necessary and provided there is sufficient sea room.

Standing Turns and Kicks Ahead
Fig. 10 and 11

Standing turns and kicks ahead can only be achieved by altering the balance between lateral resistance and rudder force, reducing the former to a minimum and then exploiting the latter to its full potential. To do this to best effect it is first necessary to take the ship's speed right down to the equivalent of dead slow or less. With the speed thus reduced, the flow of water along the ships side and therefore lateral resistance is minimal, thus allowing us to use the rudder force to greatest effect. This is best illustrated with an example of a standing turn in figure 11. In this case the same ship of 26,000t displacement is stopped in the water, with the rudder at port 35. With slow ahead the ship commences the turn and has completed 90° of that turn with an advance of only $1^1/_4$ cables or $1^1/_2$ ship lengths. This is considerably tighter than the normal turn at constant rpm for slow ahead , which is shown in figure 10 and is included for comparison as a dotted line in figure 11.

After 90° however, care should exercised as the speed is now building up. As it does so, the lateral resistance and rudder force are returning to normal and the ship is reverting to its normal, steady state, turning circle. This can be illustrated by over laying the two turning circles in figures 10 and 11. **The degree of speed reduction prior to the turn is of critical importance to tightening the turn**. Dead slow or less is the optimum and anything faster will incur a loss of turning ability.

Shallow Water
Fig. 12 and 13

So far we have only considered a ship manoeuvring in deep water. If, however, the ship is operating in shallow water it is likely to have a considerable effect upon its

Fig. 8 Slow Ahead Turns to Starboard

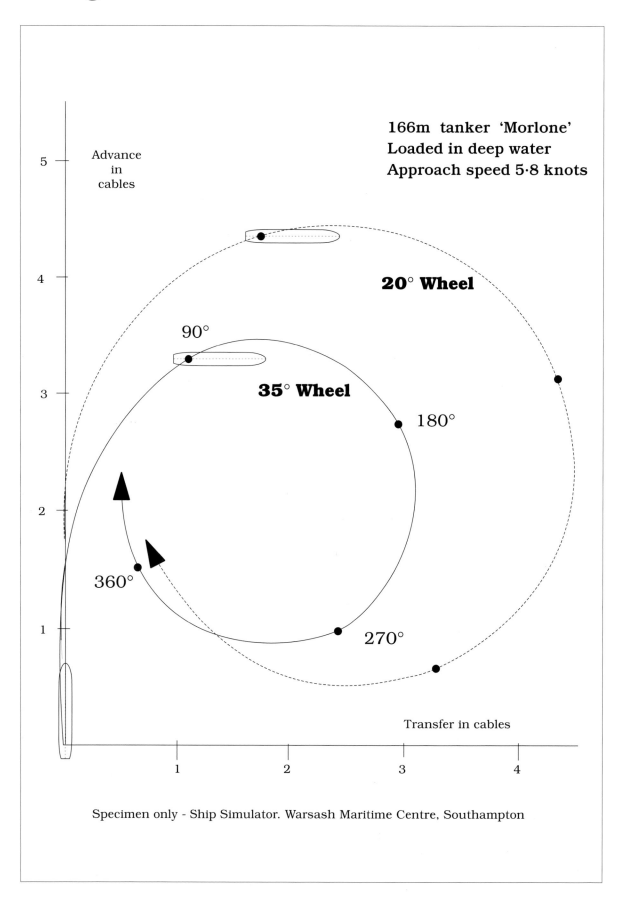

Advance in cables

166m tanker 'Morlone'
Loaded in deep water
Approach speed 5·8 knots

20° Wheel

90°

35° Wheel

180°

360°

270°

Transfer in cables

Specimen only - Ship Simulator. Warsash Maritime Centre, Southampton

Fig. 9 Full Ahead Turns to Starboard

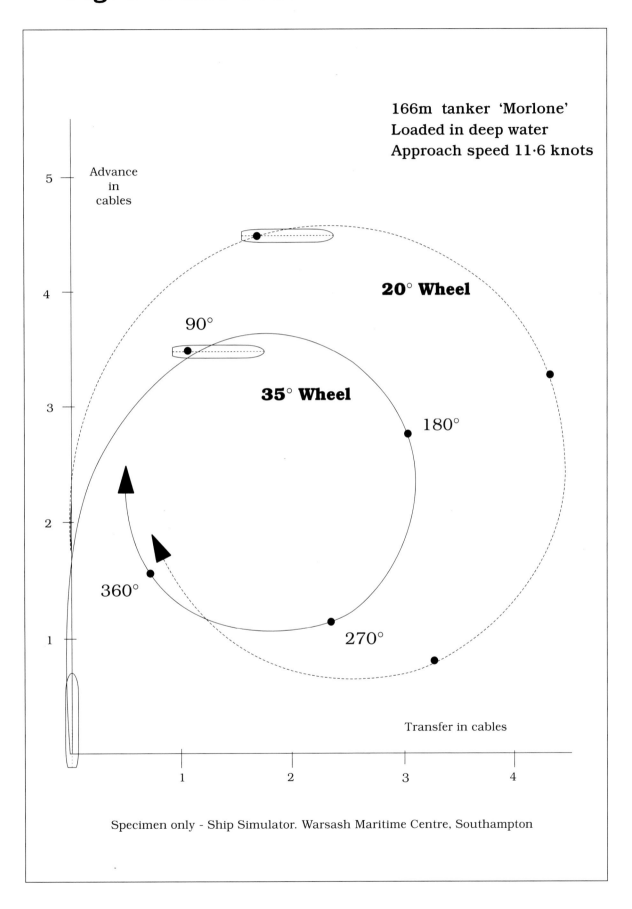

166m tanker 'Morlone'
Loaded in deep water
Approach speed 11·6 knots

5 — Advance in cables

20° Wheel

90°

35° Wheel

180°

360°

270°

Transfer in cables

Specimen only - Ship Simulator. Warsash Maritime Centre, Southampton

Fig. 10 Slow Ahead Turns to Port

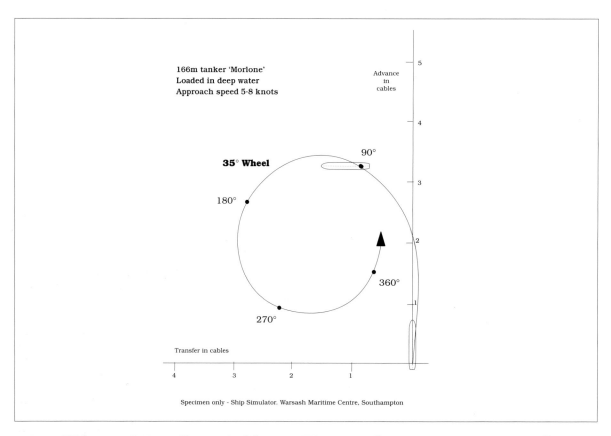

166m tanker 'Morlone'
Loaded in deep water
Approach speed 5·8 knots

Advance
in
cables

35° Wheel

90°

180°

360°

270°

Transfer in cables

Specimen only - Ship Simulator. Warsash Maritime Centre, Southampton

Fig. 11 Standing Turn from Stopped

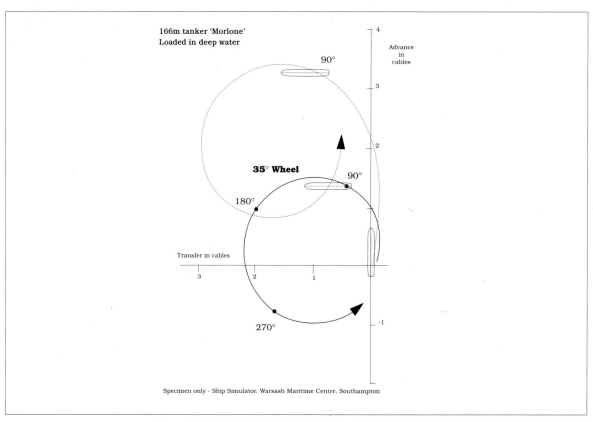

166m tanker 'Morlone'
Loaded in deep water

Advance
in
cables

90°

35° Wheel

90°

180°

270°

Transfer in cables

Specimen only - Ship Simulator. Warsash Maritime Centre, Southampton

handling characteristics and in particular its turning ability. **As a rough guide it can be assumed that a ship may experience shallow water effect when the depth of water is less than twice the draft**, i.e. the under keel clearance is less than the draft itself. Serious cases of shallow water problems have however, been experienced with larger under water clearances, especially at high speeds, sometimes with dire consequences!

To look more closely at the problem we will return to the example ship, which is fully loaded and on even keel with a draft of 12 metres. This vessel is commencing a full starboard rudder turn, with a three metre under keel clearance. Looking at the ship from astern (see figure 12a) it can be seen, as the stern of the ship commences to sweep to port, that water pressure is building up along the port side, abaft of the pivot point, due to the restriction under the keel.

In the first instance, the rudder force now has to overcome a much larger lateral resistance and is therefore considerably less efficient. Secondly, at the bow, because of the reduced under keel clearance, water which would normally pass under the ship is now restricted and there is a build up of pressure, both ahead of the ship and on the port bow. This now upsets the balance between the ships forward momentum and longitudinal resistance (see chapter 1) and pushes the pivot point back from P to PP. With the combination of these two effects, the ship is rapidly losing the rudder efficiency enjoyed in deep water.

For comparison, the deep and shallow water turns are overlaid in figure 13, and clearly illustrate the vast differences that exist between the two. This should be expected in most port approaches and harbours where, inevitably, a ship is either loaded or of a size which maximises the commercial limits of that district. Elsewhere if this is encountered without warning, perhaps during a critical turn, it is an experience never forgotten!

Draft in a Turn
Fig. 12

Finally, it should be noted that a ship manoeuvring through a large turn and influenced by shallow water may also experience an increase in draft due to list. Returning again to figure 12, it can be seen that if the under keel clearance is poor, there will be an increased pressure along the port side, which will also result in an increased flow of water under the ship. To avoid getting bogged down in complex mathematics, it is sufficient to say that this results in a low pressure under the ship, and therefore some degree of sinkage. This may be more evident with a large high sided ferry or a container ship, particularly if the ship is proceeding at high speed and already experiencing a small list due to the turn.

The amount of sinkage, in this case 1 metre, can be surprising and should not be forgotten when turning at speed in shallow water.

These effects are further considered in chapter 7 — Interaction.

Fig. 12 Effect of Shallow Water on Turning

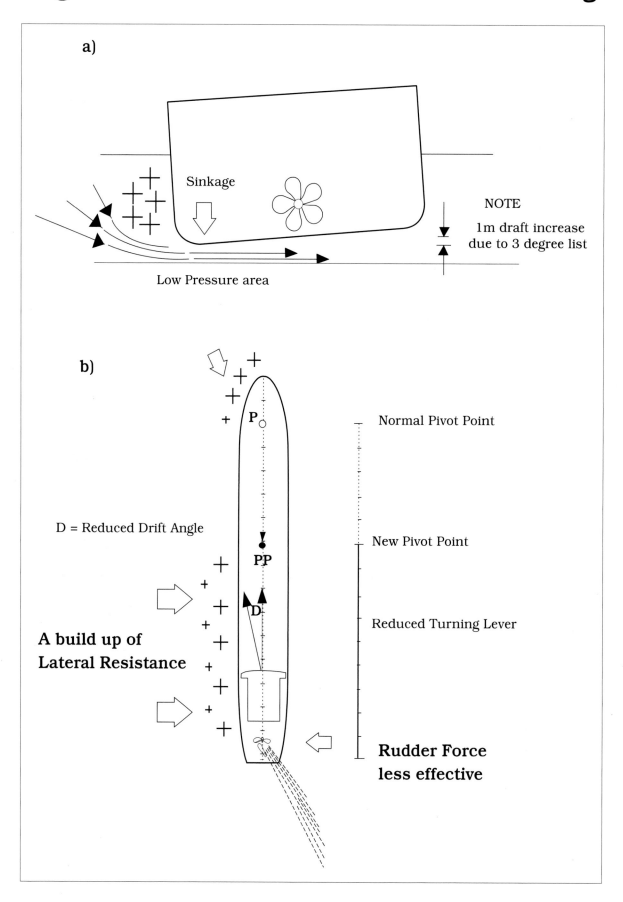

a)

Sinkage

NOTE

1m draft increase
due to 3 degree list

Low Pressure area

b)

D = Reduced Drift Angle

P

PP

D

Normal Pivot Point

New Pivot Point

Reduced Turning Lever

**A build up of
Lateral Resistance**

**Rudder Force
less effective**

Fig. 13 Turning in Shallow Water

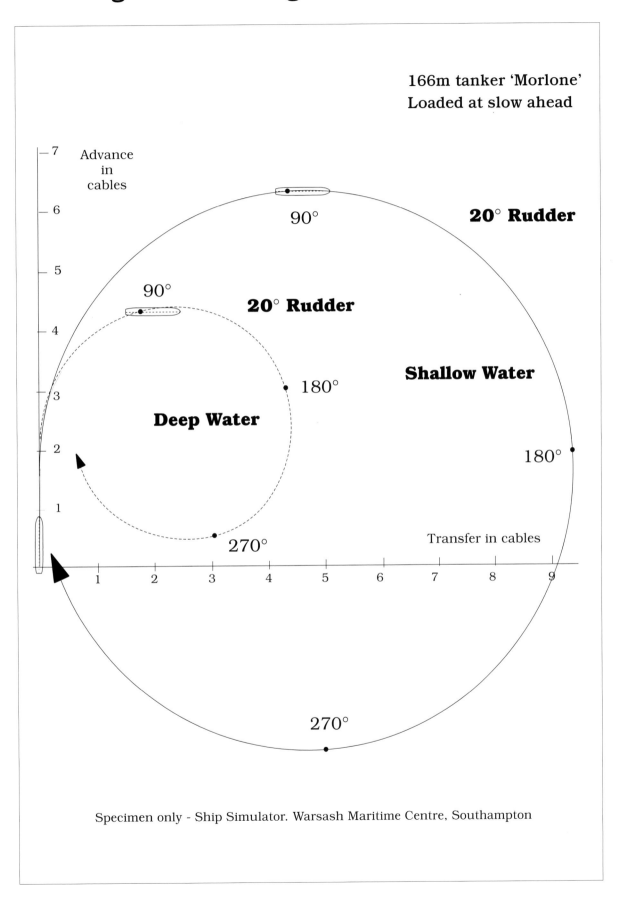

166m tanker 'Morlone'
Loaded at slow ahead

20° Rudder

20° Rudder

Shallow Water

Deep Water

Advance in cables

Transfer in cables

90°

90°

180°

180°

270°

270°

Specimen only - Ship Simulator. Warsash Maritime Centre, Southampton

Lateral Motion
Fig. 14

Whenever a kick ahead is used, provided the ship was previously stopped or at a suitably low speed, the ship initially enters into the first stage of a standing turn. The pivot point is well forward and the rudder force starts to slew the stern sideways, in a direction which is characterised, on ships with a bridge aft, by the '**drift angle**'. This is the angle between the ships head and the direction that the bridge is actually travelling in.

Once the after body is moving sideways, a large full bodied ship, such as a bulk carrier, has enormous momentum which can easily overcome lateral resistance to develop a large drift angle. In comparison, a small fine lined ship, such as a warship, might not maintain sideways motion so readily and may, therefore, not be able to develop such a large drift angle. This has a considerable effect upon the final turning circle of the respective ships, in so much that the former will usually have a good turning circle, whereas the latter may have a relatively poor turning circle.

If a ship has a large drift angle it also has the ability to generate significant sideways movement or '**lateral motion**'. This is an important characteristic and one which can be used to great advantage when handling a ship.

Fig. 14(a)

If the power is used to give a ship a good but brief kick ahead, and then taken off, the ship will be left with a residual lateral motion which can, for example, be most useful when working in towards a berth (see figure 14a). On large full bodied ships this can be very effective, with the sideways drift continuing for some time. This is particularly noticeable to an observer, in a position some way astern of the ship

The use of one or more kicks ahead will almost certainly incur the penalty of increasing headway. The ship may therefore need a little stern power to check it, before another kick ahead can be used !

Fig. 14(b)

Lateral motion can also be a disadvantage, when, for example, a ship is turning into the entrance of a channel (see figure 14b). If power is used initially to tighten the turn and then, for whatever reason, is taken off, the ship can be left with a residual lateral motion that can be extremely insidious in its effect. If a beam wind or tide is working the ship in the same direction, the effect can also be very rapid. Again, this will be more evident on a large full bodied ship, where the seemingly inexplicable sideways drift, can result in an unexpected and embarrassing situation.

It has often been noticed that those with little or no previous experience of ship handling, sometimes concentrate almost wholly on placing the bow where it is required, with no 'feel' for working a ship sideways. The ability to anticipate and feel this lateral motion, whether it be to advantage or disadvantage, is an important factor in 'seat of pants' ship handling.

Fig. 14 Lateral Motion

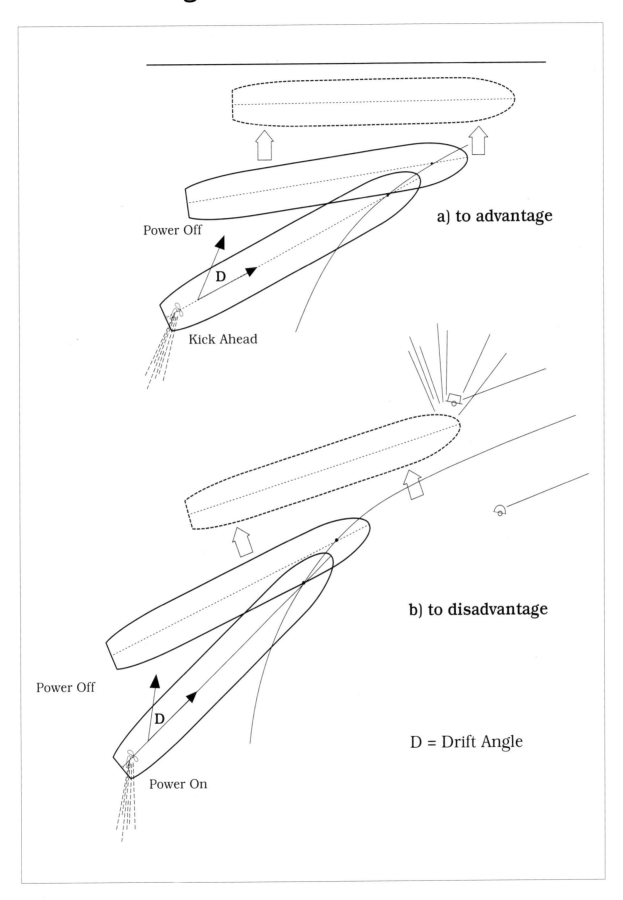

Power Off

D

Kick Ahead

a) to advantage

b) to disadvantage

Power Off

D

Power On

D = Drift Angle

CHAPTER FIVE

EFFECT OF WIND

General

THE SHIP HANDLER FACES MANY PROBLEMS but there is none more frequently experienced and less understood than the effect of wind. All too often when slowing down after a river passage, whilst entering locks and during berthing, it can create a major difficulty. With or without tugs, if the problem has not been thought out in advance, or if it is not understood how the ship will behave in the wind, the operation can get out of control extremely quickly. Needless to say, with no tug assistance it is wise to get this area of ship handling right first time and also appreciate what the limits are.

It is frequently stated by many a master that "the large funnel right aft, acts like a huge sail". Whilst this is to some extent true, it simply does not explain everything satisfactorily. It is important to look at the problem more closely.

Vessel Stopped
Fig. 15

Looking at figure 15 we have a ship on even keel, stopped dead in the water. It has the familiar all aft accommodation and we will assume, at this stage, that the wind is roughly on the beam. Whilst the large area of superstructure and funnel offer a considerable cross section to the wind, it is also necessary to take into account the area of freeboard from forward of the bridge to the bow. On a VLCC this could be an area as long as 250 x 10 metres. The centre of effort of the wind (**W**) is thus acting upon the combination of these two areas and is much further forward than is sometimes expected.

This now needs to be compared with the underwater profile of the ship and the position of the pivot point (**P**) as discussed previously. With the ship initially stopped in the water this was seen to be close to amidships. The centre of effort of the wind (**W**) and the pivot point (**P**) are thus quite close together and therefore do not create a turning influence upon the ship. Although it will vary slightly from ship to ship, generally speaking most will lay stopped with the wind just forward or just abaft the beam.

Vessel Making Headway
Fig. 16

When the same ship is making headway, the shift of the pivot point upsets the previous balance attained whilst stopped, as in figure 16. With the wind on the beam, the centre of effort of the wind remains where it is but the pivot point moves forward. This creates a substantial turning lever between **P** and **W** and, depending on wind strength, the ship will develop a swing of the bow into the wind.

This trend is compounded by the fact that at lower speeds the pivot point shifts even further forward, thereby improving the wind's turning lever and effect. It is a regrettable fact of life, when approaching a berth with the wind upon or abaft the beam, that as speed is reduced the effect of the wind gets progressively greater and requires considerable corrective action.

Fig. 15 Effect of Wind — Ship Stopped

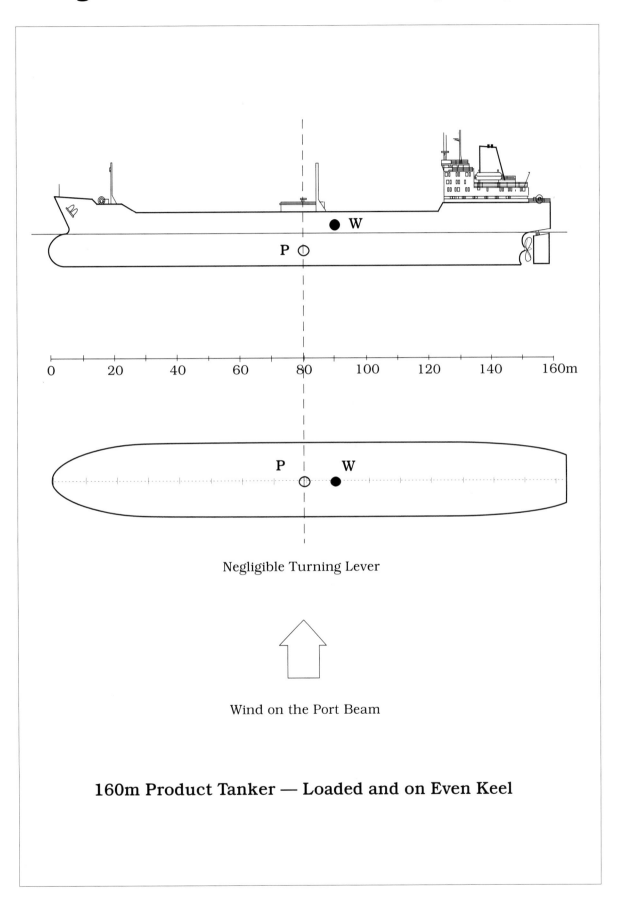

Negligible Turning Lever

Wind on the Port Beam

160m Product Tanker — Loaded and on Even Keel

Fig. 16 Effect of Wind — with Headway

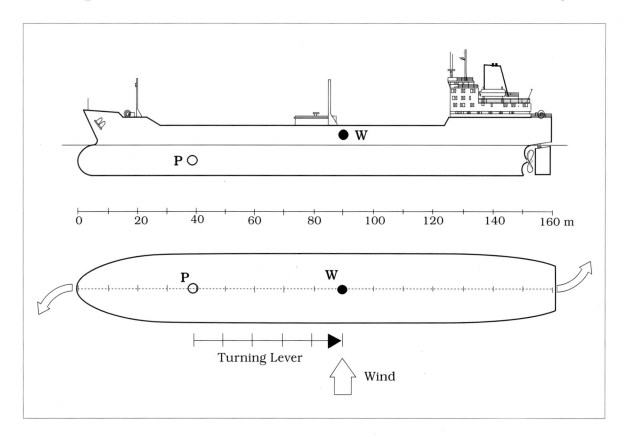

Fig. 17 Effect of Wind — with Sternway

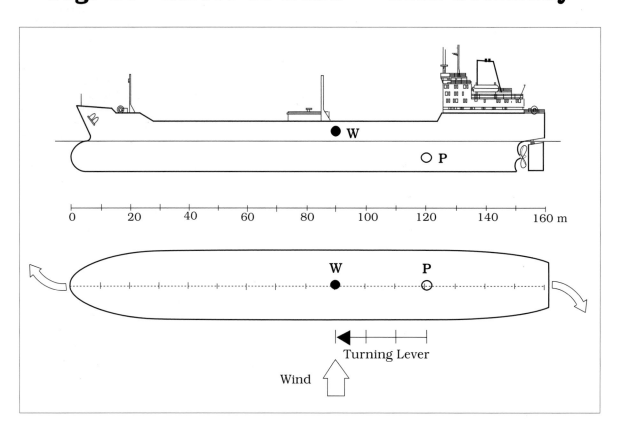

When, however, approaching a berth or a buoy with the wind dead ahead with the ship on an even keel, the approach should be much easier to control. Even at very low speeds the ship is stable and will naturally wish to stay with the wind ahead until stopped.

Vessel Making Sternway
Fig. 17

The effect of the wind on a ship making sternway is generally more complex and less predictable. In part this is due to the additional complication of transverse thrust when associated with single screw ships. Remaining with the same ship (see figure 17), we have already seen that with sternway the pivot point moves aft to a position approximately $1/4$ L from the stern. Assuming that the centre of effort (**W**) remains in the same position, with the wind still on the beam, the shift of pivot point (**P**) has now created a totally different turning lever (**WP**). This will now encourage the bow to fall off the wind when the ship is backing, or put another way, the stern seeks the wind.

Some caution is necessary, however, as the turning lever can be quite small and the effect disappointing, particularly on even keel. In such cases the stern may only partially seek the wind, with the ship making sternway 'flopped' across the wind. This situation is not helped by the centre of effort (**W**) moving aft as the wind comes round onto the quarter. This in turn tending to reduce the magnitude of the turning lever **WP**.

The other complicating factor is transverse thrust. If the wind is on the port beam, there is every likelihood that transverse thrust and effect of wind will combine and indeed take the stern smartly into the wind. If, however, the wind is on the starboard beam, it can be seen that transverse thrust and effect of wind oppose each other. Which force wins the day is therefore very much dependent upon wind strength versus stern power, unless you know the ship exceptionally well, there may be no guarantee as to which way the stern will swing when backing.

Trim and Headway
Fig. 18(a)

So far we have only considered a ship on even keel. A large trim by the stern may change the ship's handling characteristics quite substantially. Figure 18a shows the same ship, but this time in ballast and trimmed by the stern. The increase in freeboard forward has moved **W** forward and very close to **P**. With the turning lever thus reduced the ship is not so inclined to run up into the wind with headway, preferring instead to fall off, or lay across the wind. Because the ship is difficult to keep head to wind, some pilotage districts will not accept a ship that has an excessive trim by the stern, particularly with regards SBM operations.

Trim and Sternway
Fig. 18(b)

The performance when backing is also seriously altered. With the wind on the beam and **W** well forward, the turning lever **WP** is consequently increased (see figure 18b). Once the ship is stopped and particularly when backing, the bow will immediately want to fall off the wind, often with great rapidity, while the stern quickly seeks the wind.

When berthing with strong cross winds, or attempting to stop and hold in a narrow channel, it is best to plan

Fig. 18 Effect of Wind with Trim

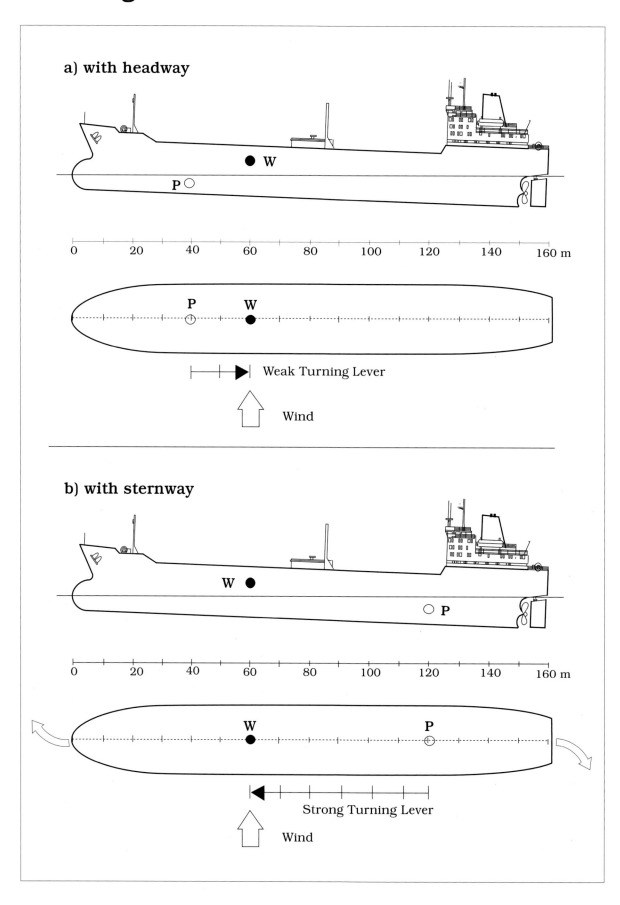

a) with headway

b) with sternway

well ahead as such a ship can prove very difficult to hold in position. However, as long as we have some prior knowledge as to how the ship will react, under the influence of the wind, it can be turned to advantage and readily employed to aid rather than hinder ship handling. Not for nothing is it often referred to as a "poor man's tug!"

Calculations

It is very useful to have a quantitative understanding of the actual force that a ship experiences whilst influenced by the wind. This may be of considerable benefit to pilots when endeavouring to estimate the wind limitations of a particular class of ship, establishing the size of tugs for a district and so forth. When confronted by the harbour authorities or charterers it is perhaps better, in the interests of professionalism, to be armed with concrete facts rather than simply say "we don't think it can be done". Worse, is to be forced to attempt a movement with unacceptable risks.

Whilst complicated formulae do exist, for calculating the force of wind upon a ship, it would be more practical to have at hand a relatively simple method of achieving a working figure. The first requirement is to obtain the best available estimation of the area of the ship presented to the wind in square metres, if it were on the beam. This can be as simple as ......

Length overall (m) x max. freeboard (m) will give an approximation of the total windage area (m²).

An approximate wind force in tonnes per 1,000 m² can then be calculated using:

If V = Wind Speed (metres/second)

$$= \frac{\text{Wind speed (Knots)}}{2}$$

then

$$\textbf{Force (tonnes) per 1000 m}^2 = \frac{V^2}{18}$$

It should be noted that the wind force varies as the square of the wind speed. Small increases in wind speed can mean large increases in wind strength, especially in stronger winds, when gusting can place an enormous strain on the ship.

Examples
Fig. 19, 20 and 21

Using the above formulae, this is illustrated (see figure 19) with the graphs of wind force (tonnes) over a wide range of wind speeds (knots) for a 60,000 dwt tanker and a large 197m car carrier.

Ships in the category of the 60,000 dwt tanker may have a main engine capacity of around 15,000 shp at sea speed. This is equivalent to about 150 tonnes force. It is broken down to give a rough approximation for dead slow to manoeuvring full speed in figure 20.

Kicks ahead with full rudder will, at best, be somewhere in the region of 45% of these figures.

Fig. 19 Graph of Wind Forces

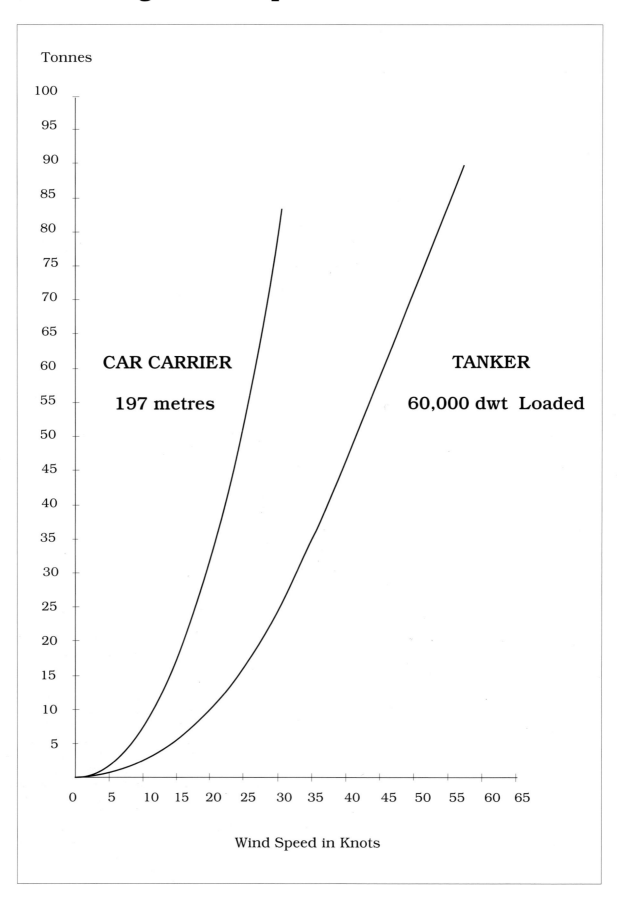

Tonnes

CAR CARRIER

197 metres

TANKER

60,000 dwt Loaded

Wind Speed in Knots

Fig. 20 Comparison of Forces 1 — Tanker

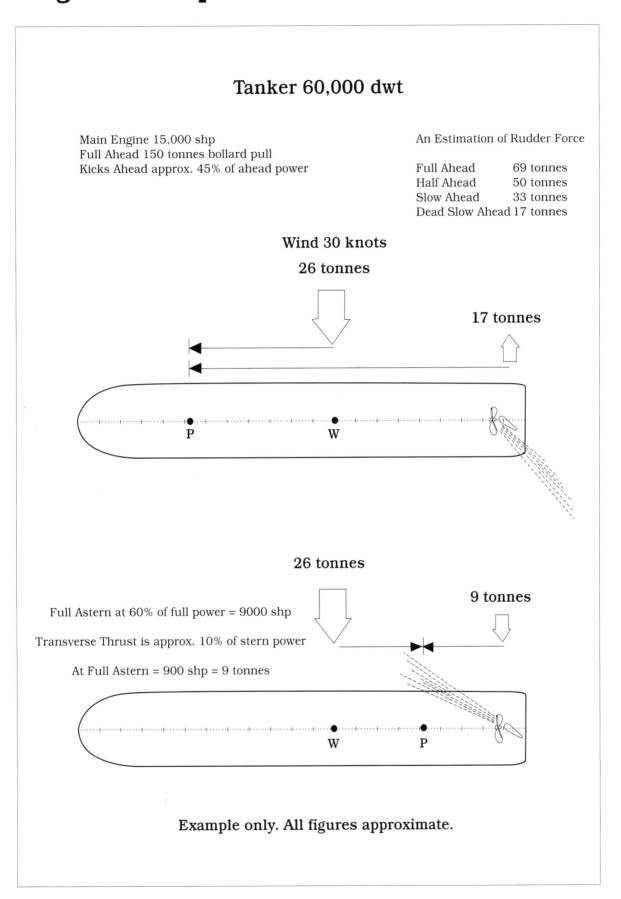

Tanker 60,000 dwt

Main Engine 15,000 shp
Full Ahead 150 tonnes bollard pull
Kicks Ahead approx. 45% of ahead power

An Estimation of Rudder Force

Full Ahead   69 tonnes
Half Ahead   50 tonnes
Slow Ahead   33 tonnes
Dead Slow Ahead 17 tonnes

Wind 30 knots

26 tonnes

17 tonnes

P   W

26 tonnes

9 tonnes

Full Astern at 60% of full power = 9000 shp

Transverse Thrust is approx. 10% of stern power

At Full Astern = 900 shp = 9 tonnes

W   P

Example only. All figures approximate.

Fig. 21 Comparison of Forces 2 — Car Carrier
(when attempting to thrust sideways)

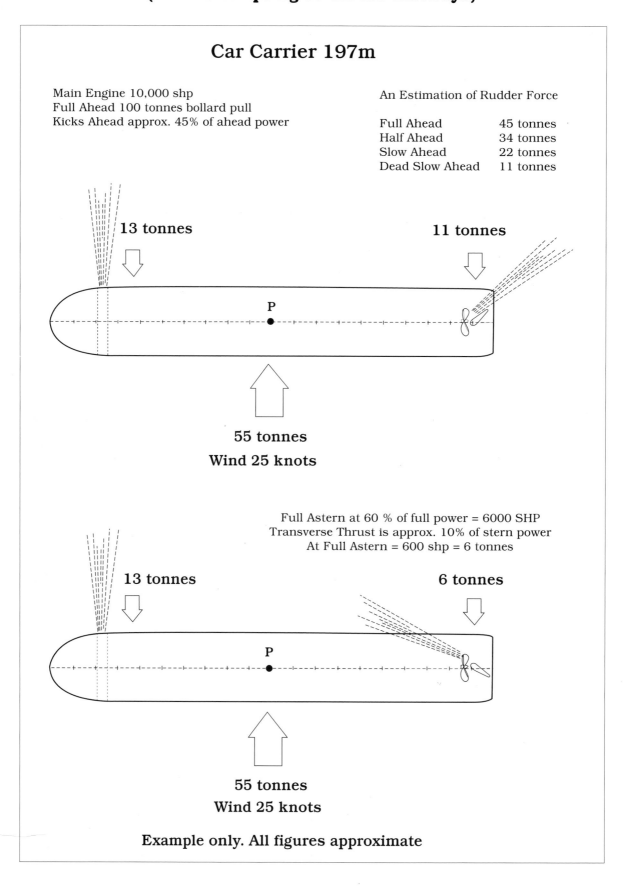

Car Carrier 197m

Main Engine 10,000 shp
Full Ahead 100 tonnes bollard pull
Kicks Ahead approx. 45% of ahead power

An Estimation of Rudder Force

Full Ahead	45 tonnes
Half Ahead	34 tonnes
Slow Ahead	22 tonnes
Dead Slow Ahead	11 tonnes

13 tonnes

11 tonnes

P

55 tonnes

Wind 25 knots

Full Astern at 60 % of full power = 6000 SHP
Transverse Thrust is approx. 10% of stern power
At Full Astern = 600 shp = 6 tonnes

13 tonnes

6 tonnes

P

55 tonnes

Wind 25 knots

Example only. All figures approximate

Similarly, if we assume stern power to be a little over half that of ahead power, we can compile an approximate list of the range of stern powers.

Transverse thrust may be no more than 10% of these figures.

A similar exercise is outlined in figure 21 for the car carrier with a 10,000 shp main engine. This type of ship may also be fitted with a bow thruster, of 1,000 kW (1341 shp or 13 tonnes) for example, and it is interesting to compare the combined efforts of the main engine and the bow thruster when endeavouring to hold the ship against a beam wind.

Summary

By comparing the wind force at its worse, i.e. on the beam, with the forces available to the ship handler, including tugs, several important points come to light ......

- **Kicks ahead with full power are very effective against a wide range of wind strengths.**

- **Kicks ahead of dead slow and slow will be ineffective at certain wind strengths and more power must be used.**

- **The weakness of transverse thrust as a force.**

- **The likely wind strength at which the transverse thrust will be overcome by the wind.**

- **The limits of the bow thruster in beam winds.**

- **The size of tugs required for that class of ship, or its wind limits with the operational tugs in a specific port.**

This information is of course extremely basic, referring in the main to a ship which is initially stopped in the water, on even keel and with a beam wind. Ships like passenger vessels with high 'rounded' superstructures generate considerable aerodynamic lift in a wind which can change the balance of forces. It is, nevertheless, surprisingly accurate to use the 'slab sided' effect, as trials have shown, and more than adequate for practical purposes.

The view aft from a tug showing the towing arrangements directly from a winch

CHAPTER SIX

DREDGING ANCHORS

General

IN THE COASTAL TRADES OF EUROPE small ships frequently resort to dredging anchors when berthing, as an aid in confined areas, often in difficult tidal and wind conditions. On larger tonnage, with the exception of a limited number of pilotage districts, or in cases of emergencies, it is an art which over the last two of three decades has declined in usage. This may be for fear of damaging the anchor equipment, on the generally larger ships which are common today. Such reservations are unnecessary if the equipment is used correctly and within the operational limitations of the anchor, cable and windlass. Few opportunities exist on board ship to practice specific areas of ship handling and this is also a difficult aspect of ship handling to simulate in electronic simulators. It is on the other hand, an area in which manned models excel, offering every opportunity for experimentation and practice.

Local Knowledge

It goes without saying that the type of sea bed is of paramount importance to dredging, soft mud being the most obvious choice. The bottom must also be free of obstructions such as power lines, pipes and rock, therefore good local knowledge is essential. As the anchors normally dredge just inside the lines of the ship, there must also be adequate under keel clearance to avoid damaging the hull. This is also very much a question of local knowledge and may vary considerably from one district to another. It is never the less interesting to note, that in one district, ships of up to 120,000 dwt frequently dredge two anchors, sometimes on flat rock, to assist control when berthing without tugs. Damaging an anchor or windlass far outweighs the risk of serious damage to ship or quay!

The Windlass

Research has shown that whilst the anchors and the cable are relatively reliable, the windlass is not. This is partly due to the disproportionate size of a windlass on the much larger ship of today. A 1000% increase in tonnage has only been matched with a 250% increase in the size of anchor gear. There has been some evidence to suggest that this weakness is likely to exist in ships over 50,000 dwt. In addition it should be remembered that the kinetic energy created by a ship in excess of 50,000 dwt, moving over the ground in any direction, at more than say 0.3 knot, is enormous. By comparison, windlasses may only be capable of lifting a small minimum design weight, as specified by the classification societies. This is the weight of the anchor and four shackles of cable, hanging dead in the water and therefore nothing in comparison to the full weight of the ship. If all of this energy is imparted into the anchor it has to go somewhere and it is usually to the windlass. The dissipation of such energy often being seen as brake or gear failure!

Safety Parameters

The source material for this chapter is based upon extensive research by the classification societies. It is from this that we can establish the safety parameters within which to operate when dredging anchors.

- The amount of cable in the water should not exceed **1¹/₂ x depth of water** (some sources quote 2 x depth). If this figure is exceeded the anchor is likely to dig in and commence holding.

- The design speed of a windlass gypsy in gear is about 30 feet/minute which is approximately 3 minutes a shackle. This is equal to a ship speed of **0.3 knots over the ground.** (assuming the UK shackle of 15 fathoms / 90 feet / 27.2m)

- The windlass is only designed to lift the dead weight of the anchor and four shackles.

If, therefore, the amount of cable in the water does not exceed 1¹/₂ x depth, we have a safety factor which guards against speeds in excess of 0.3 knots, because the anchors will not dig in and hold, but drag (some companies use 0.5 knots).

When the amount of cable exceeds 1¹/₂ x depth, the speed must be below 0.3 knots, especially if the windlass is in gear or the brake is screwed up. The anchor will most certainly dig in and attempt to hold the full weight of the ship.

Each shipping company has its own specific standing orders for anchoring large ships and these should be adhered to at all times.

Letting Go

On smaller ships, when pilots are putting out anchors for dredging purposes, it is customary to 'let go' with the anchor on the brake. On large ships, however, with unknown equipment and crews of mixed nationality and capability, it may be appropriate to walk out the anchors in gear rather than let them go on the brake. This affords the pilot much more control over the operation, guarding against the crew 'screwing up' the brake with the wrong amount of cable out, or worse still, letting the cable run away, leaving the pilot with 12 shackles out on both anchors!

Dredging Two Anchors
Fig. 22

Dredging is remarkably effective at eliminating the two major problems that occur when berthing without tugs; firstly control of heading and secondly control over speed. The effect of dredging can be seen in figure 22. The ship is conducting a dredge with two anchors, working into a port side berthing position. By dredging the two anchors the pivot point is brought right forward between the two windlasses. This gives the ship a much improved and excellent steering lever. The small weight of the two anchors, dragging along on the sea bed, is also surprisingly effective in controlling the speed of the ship. Even whilst maintaining dead slow revolutions, the ship may gradually slow down and stop. This in turn ensures that the pivot point remains forward and that lateral resistance, which would otherwise oppose turning ability, is also kept low throughout.

The net result is an ability to keep the speed down, but at the same time use main power more efficiently, when controlling heading with kicks ahead. The bow can virtually

Fig. 22 Dredging Two Anchors

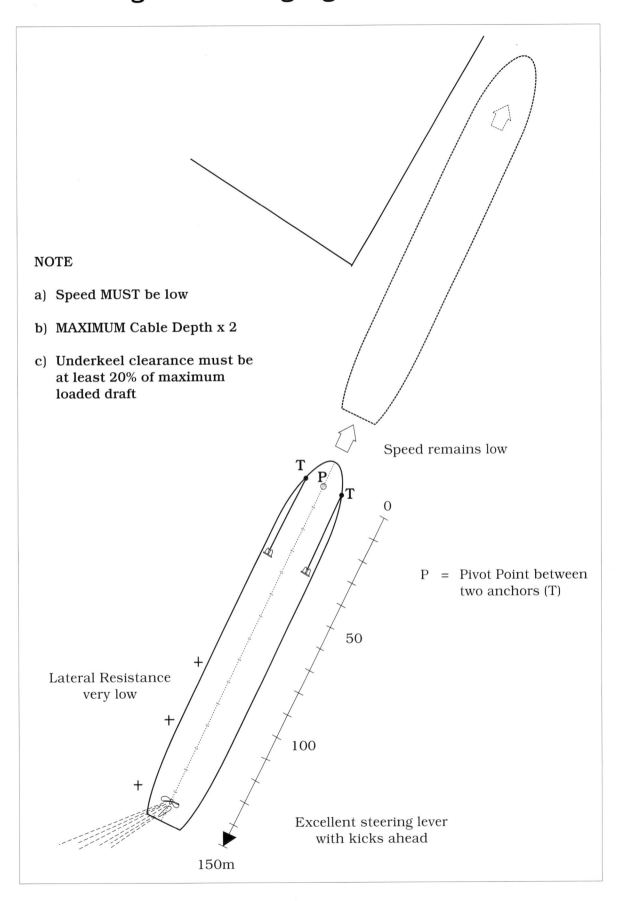

NOTE

a) Speed MUST be low

b) MAXIMUM Cable Depth x 2

c) Underkeel clearance must be at least 20% of maximum loaded draft

Speed remains low

T

P

T

0

P = Pivot Point between two anchors (T)

50

Lateral Resistance very low

100

Excellent steering lever with kicks ahead

150m

Fig. 23 Dredging One Anchor

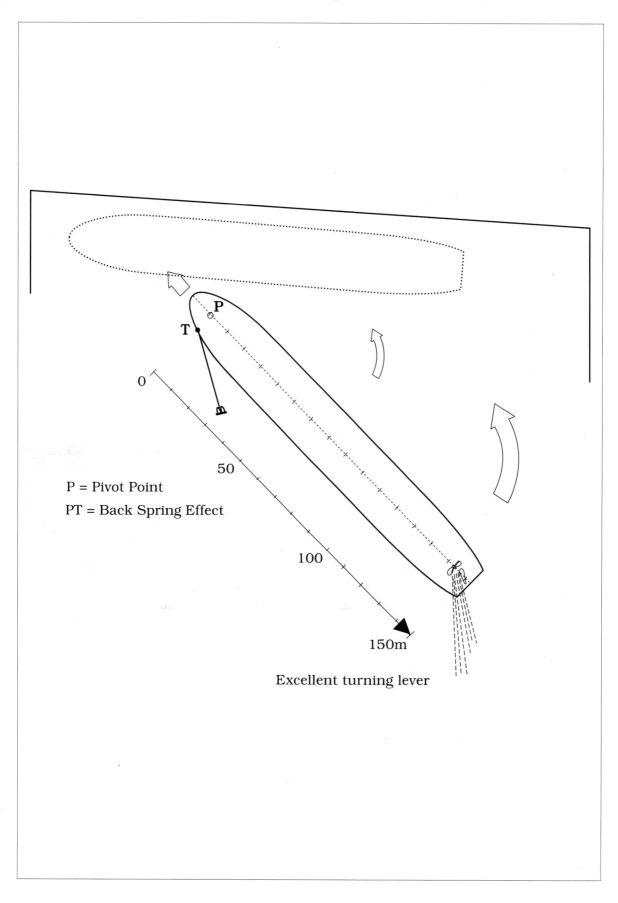

0

50

100

150m

P = Pivot Point

PT = Back Spring Effect

T

P

Excellent turning lever

**This model shows well the anchoring arrangements
which are used to demonstrate dredging techniques**

be driven on the anchors, to the desired position and, more to the point, it will remain there. At the same time, the old enemy, speed, is kept well under control!

Some masters may express concern, as to whether the two anchors being dredged will foul each other, while the ship is turning. The answer to this is no, because if the ratio of cable to depth of water is correct, one anchor simply cannot reach the cable of the other. They should also be easy to recover once alongside.

Dredging One Anchor
Fig. 23

Generally speaking, because pilots and masters have more experience of dredging one anchor than two, the question is frequently asked, "Why dredge two anchors?". The answer is relatively simple, because dredging one anchor only achieves 50% of the effect, which could otherwise be gained by dredging two anchors. It is not possible to use anything like the same amount of power for positioning the bow and the speed is nowhere near as easy to control.

By using one anchor, particularly on large beamed ships, it should be remembered that the pivot point is moved out to the ship's side (see figure 23). This creates an effective turning moment **PT** in much the same manner as a back spring, which can quite clearly be felt and needs constant counter helm to correct. This can be irritating if a straight line approach is desired. On the other hand, if a large turn in confined waters, is necessary prior to berthing, then this tendency can obviously be utilised and turned to great advantage, with the single anchor being viewed effectively as a back spring. The validity of this should be considered when deciding whether to deploy one or two anchors.

Important Points when Dredging

There is a very fine line between the success or failure of a dredging operation. The following points are crucial in order to achieve the desired results:-

- **Maintain the normal slow speed of approach prior to letting go, or walking out, the anchors.** If the ship is stopped, the anchors will dig in and it is then difficult to get underway again. The ship may also drift badly out of position.

- **Walk the anchors out as early as possible.** This gives sufficient time to get the feel of the ship before the berth is reached. It is recommended, if practicable, in order to avoid underwater damage to the hull, that the ship's under keel clearance should be at least 20% of that vessels maximum loaded draft.

- **Do not let the ship stop too early.** This lets the anchor flukes drop and dig in and it then takes substantial power to get the ship underway again.

- **Do not let the speed build up.** This pushes the pivot point back to its normal position. Consequently the anchors cease to be effective and are of no use.

- **Do not exceed $1^1/_2$ x depth.** It is possible, however, especially on small ships, to 'feel' the anchors and adjust the amount of cable accordingly.

- **Keep the weight on the anchors.** Backing the ship will take the weight off the cables and they become ineffective.

- **Avoid rushing the operation,** particularly swinging, on large ships. There should only be a gentle and steady strain on the cable(s); the manoeuvre being slow but very effective.

- **Once in position** on the berth, slack back the cables as the tension in them is sufficient to pull the ship back.

CHAPTER SEVEN

INTERACTION

Introduction

THE FILM 'INTERACTION' (see references) which to date has probably been seen by thousands of seafarers, is without doubt extremely good value. Despite its age the content is still good and very relevant. This is another area where manned model training excels in giving officers every opportunity to take the ship models in close to a bank, or another model, at various speeds and experience the effects of interaction for real. The models are very strong, having survived some spectacular collisions and groundings over the years, and as such this is the best way to gain invaluable experience, better than one day, too late on a real ship!

Bank Effect

Fig. 24 and 25

When a ship is making headway, a positive pressure area builds up forward of the pivot point, whilst aft of the pivot point the flow of water down the ships side creates a low pressure area (see figure 24). This area extends out from the ship and in deep, open water, clear of other traffic, is not a problem.

If however the ship commences to close a vertical obstruction, such as a shoal or canal bank, the area experiences some degree of restriction and the ship will be influenced by the resultant forces which build up. It is often thought that the positive pressure at the bow is the main problem, probably because of the tendency to relate most channel work to the bow and heading. Looking at figure 25, it can be seen that whilst the pressure at the bow is important, it is only working on a short turning lever forward of the pivot point. The low pressure or suction area is, on the other hand, working well aft of the pivot point and consequently is a very strong force.

As a result of these two forces which have developed, the stern of the ship is likely to be sucked into the bank. It can be very difficult to break out of its hold, the ship requiring constant corrective rudder and power, sometimes hard over, in order to control heading.

Excessive speed must be avoided as, yet again, it is a crucial factor in creating a 'bank effect' problem, because the magnitude of the forces varies with the square of the ships speed or water flow.

Squat

Fig. 26

So far we have only considered a vertical obstruction in the vicinity of the ship. Should it also be running in shallow water, **with a depth of less than twice the draft**, an additional obstruction exists which can seriously compound the problem. This is illustrated in figure 26 where the ship is running on an even keel with a small under keel clearance. Therefore water which would normally pass under the ship is severely restricted.

This results in two things. Firstly, the water being forced under the bow at a higher speed than normal creates a low pressure and loss of buoyancy (see figure 26a). Secondly, the buildup of water ahead of the ship increases

Fig. 24 Pressure Zones (simplified)

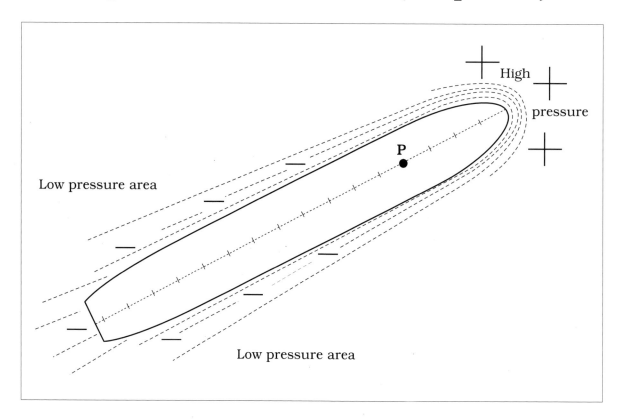

Fig. 25 Bank Effect

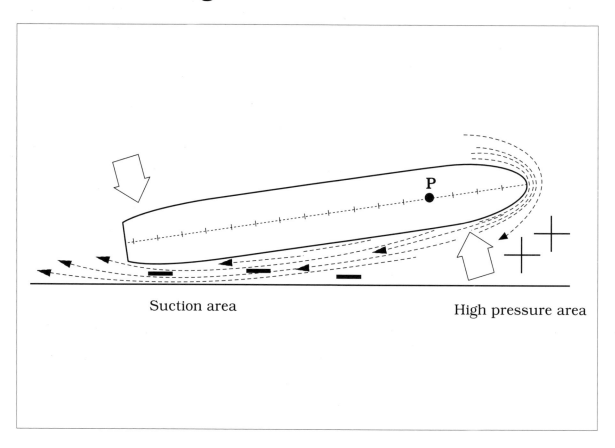

Fig. 26 Effect of Trim and Squat

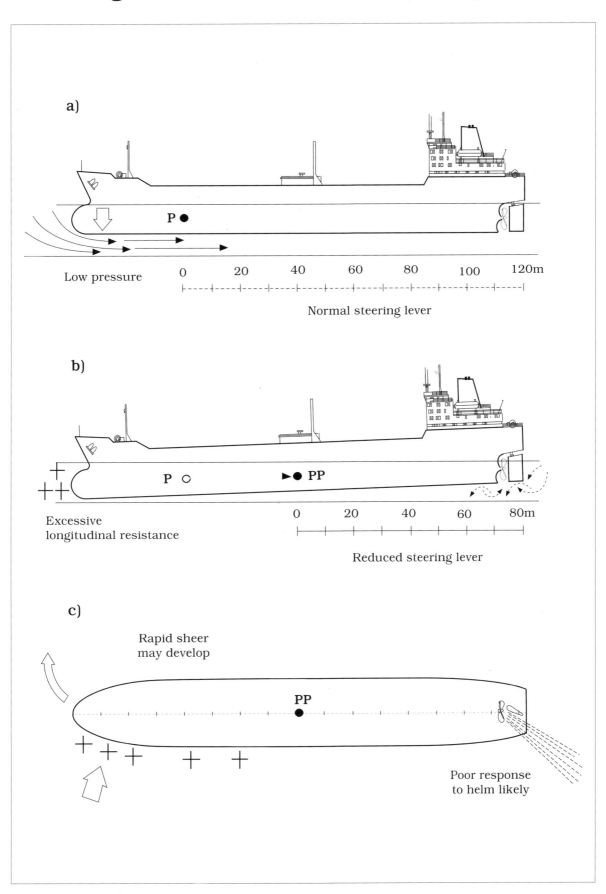

a)

Low pressure

0   20   40   60   80   100   120m

Normal steering lever

b)

P ○   ▶● PP

Excessive
longitudinal resistance

0   20   40   60   80m

Reduced steering lever

c)

Rapid sheer
may develop

PP

Poor response
to helm likely

Fig. 27 Bank Configuration

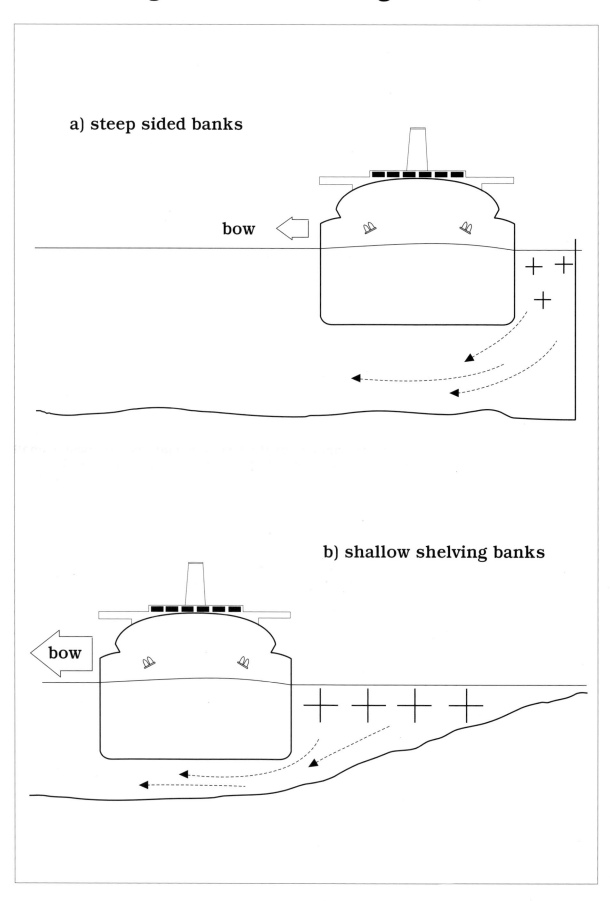

a) steep sided banks

bow

b) shallow shelving banks

bow

longitudinal resistance and pushes the pivot point back from **P** to **PP** and the steering lever is reduced (see figure 26b). The ship will now 'squat by the bow' which in turn makes the problem even worse. Several cases have been reported of large ships running in shallow water and experiencing bow sinkage of up to 2 metres!

The ship's wave system, catching a ship up as it slows in shallow water, may also affect trim for a short time and enhance sinkage at the bow.

In addition to the possibility of grounding forward there also exists the possibility of losing control and sheering violently out of a channel. If the helmsman allows a small swing to develop, longitudinal pressure forces will be brought round onto the exposed bow (see figure 26c) and this will in turn encourage a violent swing in the same direction as the helm. Counter helm to correct the swing may be sluggish because, as we have seen, the steering lever is reduced. Once the ship does respond, it may now sheer violently the other way. A chain reaction then sets in, with the ship sheering badly from one side to the other and failing to respond correctly to the helm. The effect can be extremely rapid, with the ship out of the channel and aground in just a few minutes.

Excessive speed is the main contributing factor under such circumstance and reduced speeds are essential to avoid such violent forces building up.

Trim is also important and in some districts the pilotage authority may refuse to handle certain ships if they are trimmed by the head and may even request a small trim by the stern. The latter does, in any case, improve the steering lever and therefore the handling of a ship. It may also be intended as an allowance for squat by the bow and is very much a decision based upon local knowledge and experience.

It should, however, be noted that when a ship is trimmed by the stern it is possible, with propeller action, for the loss of buoyancy due to low pressure under the hull, to accentuate the stern trim. It 'surprised' many observers to find out that a large passenger vessel travelling at speed in shallow water grounded at the stern.

Shallow Water
Fig. 27(a) and (b)

It would be wrong to imply that bank effect is only experienced within the domain of canals and rivers with steep sided banks, as illustrated in figure 27a. To a ship running in shallow water, with adjacent but gently shelving mud or sand banks, such as low lying estuarial areas, figure 27b, the effect can be far more insidious and violent.

There are many cases, in the archives of casualty investigation, where groundings and collisions have occurred in such areas, due to drastic loss of control, whilst the ship was under the combined influence of both shallow water and bank effect.

One noticeable feature in some of these casualties is the tendency of the master immediately to reduce revolutions, or even stop the engine, when faced with the ship sheering the wrong way and apparently failing to respond to progressively larger angles of helm. Hard over rudder and a healthy 'kick ahead' are essential to regaining control.

These are of course generalities and every event is dictated by its own unique set of circumstances.

It is clear that many ships work daily in shallow water without any problems whatsoever. Just occasionally, however, all the ingredients of shallow water, bank effect, excessive speed and poor trim come together and combine in an insidious manner to create another casualty.

Ship to Ship Interaction

It is clear thus far that a great deal of caution needs to be shown when operating in narrow and shallow waters. It almost goes without saying that extreme care is needed, if, intentionally or otherwise, another ship is brought into this dangerous scenario, with involvement in an overtaking or passing situation. It is essential to be aware of the forces at work.

Passing

In the interests of both simplicity and clarity the sequence of events during a 'meeting end on' manoeuvre are illustrated with three diagrams.

Phase 1
Fig. 28

It is important at this stage, when meeting another ship, not to work over to the starboard side of the channel too early or too far. If the ship gets too close to a shoal or bank it can experience bank effect and unexpectedly sheer across the path of the approaching ship with appalling consequences.

As the two bows approach each other, the combined bow pressure zones between them will build up and encourage the respective bows to turn away from each other. Helm may be required to check the swing.

Phase 2
Fig. 29

With the two ships nearly abeam of each other, a combined low pressure, or suction area exists between them and, if the vessels are too close together, there is every likelihood of them being sucked together in a collision. Literally!

At this stage the bow of each ship will also begin to smell the low pressure area astern of the other. It is usual to feel this 'turning in' towards the other ship as you pass and it is helpful because it is also back towards the centre of the channel.

Phase 3
Fig. 30

Having previously turned in towards the centre of the channel, the opposite now occurs. As the two sterns pass each other, they are drawn together by the low pressure area between them and this has a tendency to realign the ships with the channel.

These effects are not always very noticeable, because the ships often pass through the pressure zones fairly quickly, even at relatively slow speeds. The effects however should always be anticipated and used correctly to advantage, corrective helm being applied when necessary.

Fig. 28 Passing — Phase 1

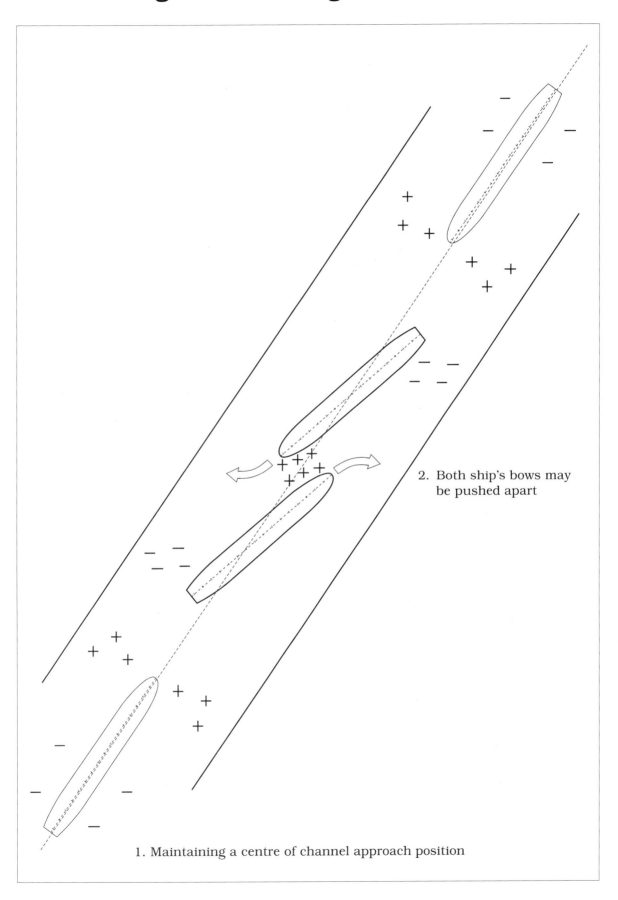

2. Both ship's bows may be pushed apart

1. Maintaining a centre of channel approach position

Fig. 29 Passing — Phase 2

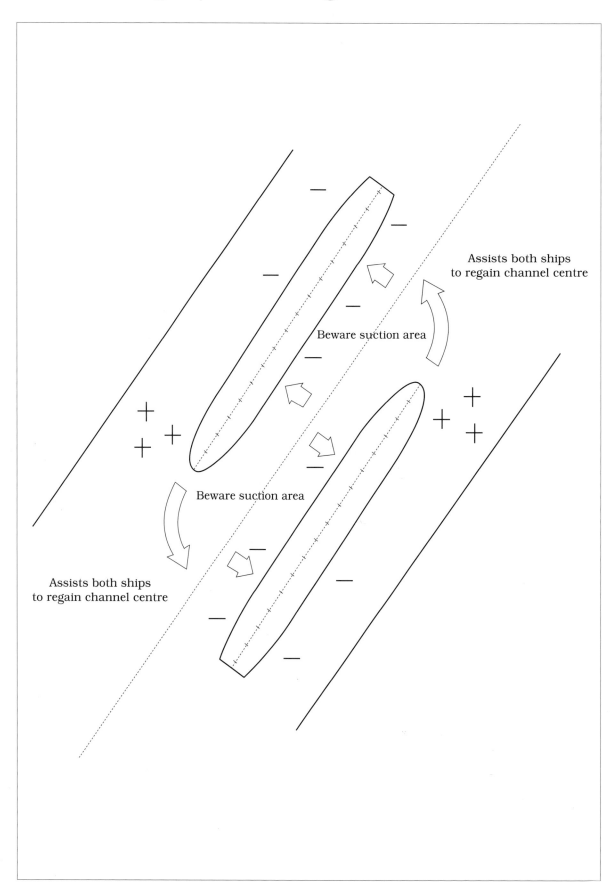

Assists both ships
to regain channel centre

Beware suction area

Beware suction area

Assists both ships
to regain channel centre

Fig. 30 Passing — Phase 3

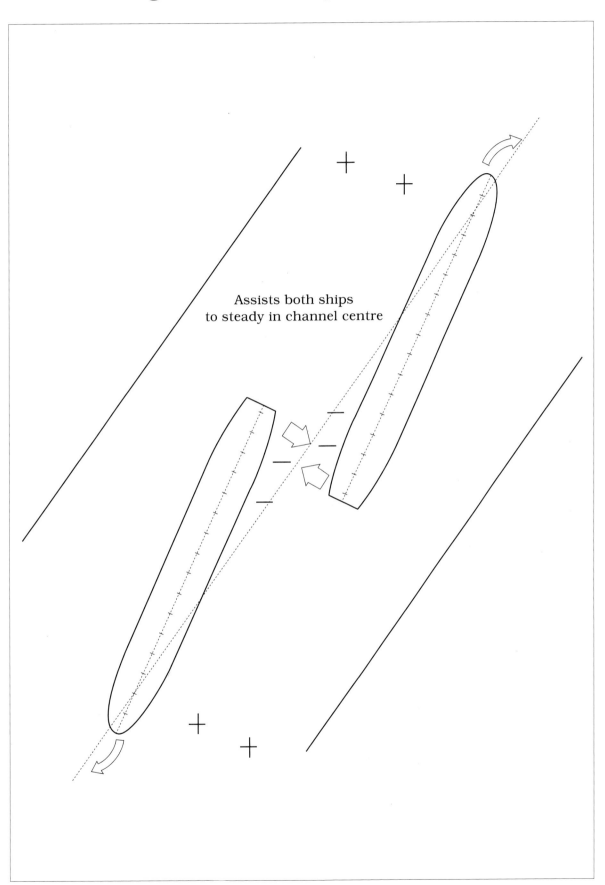

Assists both ships
to steady in channel centre

Overtaking

Similarly for the sake of clarity, the 'overtaking' operation is also discussed with just three illustrations.

Phase 1
Fig. 31

The ship to be overtaken should not move over to the starboard side of the channel without first considering the consequences of bank effect and the danger of shearing across the path of the overtaking vessel. This particularly applies to smaller vessels, which will easily be influenced by a larger ship.

As ship A approaches the stern of ship B its bow pressure zone will put pressure on the rudder of ship B causing it to shear across the path of the overtaking vessel.

The overtaking ship A will also feel the low pressure area astern of B and exhibit a tendency to turn in towards the stern of the other ship.

Ship B may experience an increase in speed, as it is virtually pushed along by the pressure zone of the overtaking ship.

These can be very powerful forces, and it may require full rudder and power to counteract them!

Phase 2
Fig. 32

With the two ships abeam of each other, a powerful pressure zone exists between their bows and a low pressure area between their sterns. These combine to produce a strong turning lever which is trying to swing the bows away from each other. This is a powerful force and vigorous corrective measures may again be needed.

In addition to the turning forces, there is also an underlying suction area between the two ships which will, if they are allowed to get too close, draw then inexorably alongside of each other. If this does happen, ship B is normally dragged along with ship A and unless they both slow down together, to relax the suction area between them, it is especially difficult to get the two ships apart again.

At this stage ship B may revert to its original propeller speed and appear to slow down in relation to the other vessel.

Phase 3
Figure 33

As the overtaking ship passes the other vessel, ship B, may be influenced by the effects of two powerful forces. Firstly on one side, bank effect and secondly, on the other side, the low pressure area of the passing vessel. This can combine as a very strong turning force and require bold corrective action.

The rudder of ship A may be adversely effected with positive pressure, as it passes through the pressure zone around the bow of the overtaken ship B, particularly if that ship is large. This can cause ship A ship to turn unexpectedly across the path of the overtaken ship.

As ship B is drawn towards the suction area of the passing ship, it may experience a noticeable increase in speed.

Fig. 31 Overtaking — Phase 1

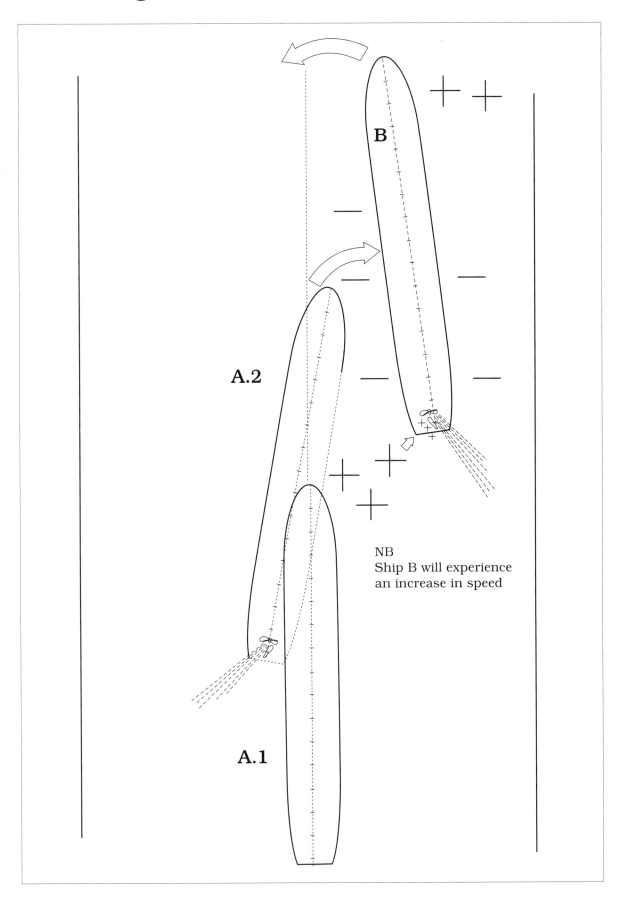

B

A.2

A.1

NB
Ship B will experience
an increase in speed

Fig. 32 Overtaking — Phase 2

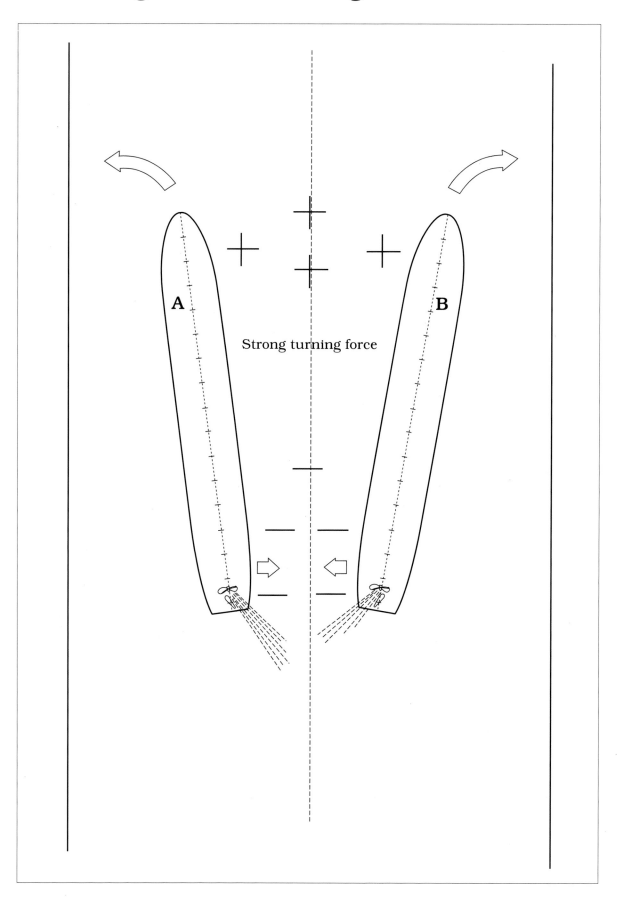

Strong turning force

Fig. 33 Overtaking — Phase 3

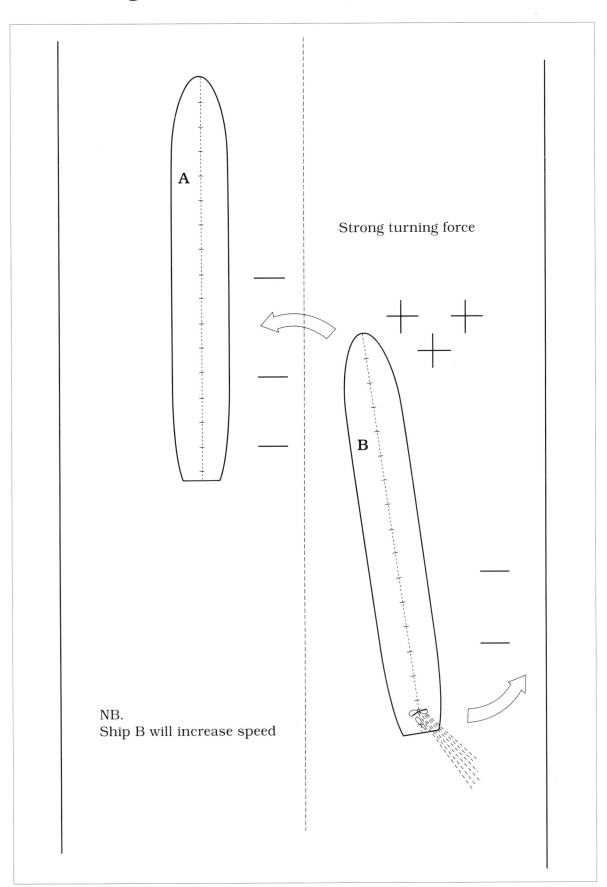

A

Strong turning force

B

NB.
Ship B will increase speed

General points

The following general points should be noted ......

- **prior to the manoeuvre each ship remains in the centre of the channel for a long as possible**. Failure to do so could expose either ship to bank effect, leading to a sheer across the path of the oncoming ship, or grounding.

- **speed should be low to reduce the interactive forces**. There is, then, plenty of reserve power for the use of corrective 'kicks ahead'.

- **if the ships pass from deep to shallow water** at any time during the manoeuvre, the forces will increase drastically and extreme caution should be exercised.

- **the smaller of two ships and tugs, are likely to be the most seriously affected**. Large ships should be aware of this and adjust their speed accordingly.

- figures 28 through 33 illustrate the anticipated sheers that may develop throughout each manoeuvre and the maximum corrective helm that may be required, in this case 35°.

- the engines should be brought to dead slow ahead for the manoeuvre, particularly turbine or fixed pitch propeller ships, so that power is instantly available to control the ship with 'kicks ahead'.

- on completion of the manoeuvre each ship should regain the centre of the channel as quickly as possible to avoid any furtherance of bank effect.

- it should be appreciated that pilots who are engaged in canal work all the time become very specialised in this area and their advice should always be sought when in doubt.

Summary

It should be stressed that in these notes, as with all the preceding chapters, every effort has been made to strike a balance between what is considered essential theoretical content and practical application. The notes were originally intended to be supplementary to manned model work, which support and put into practice much of the content by giving individuals, follow up 'hands on' practical experience.

**Ships and tugs operating in confined waters have to be aware
of the effects of interaction**

CHAPTER EIGHT

EFFECT OF TIDE

General

To THOSE PERSONNEL that have been able to gain experience in handling a ship within a tidal district, it may seem surprising that a high proportion of those less experienced officers often express concern as to how a tide or current will affect the handling characteristics of a ship. Whilst on the one hand it is possible to offer easy explanations concerning the effect of the tide, it is on the other hand difficult, because the tidal flow in and around jetties and waterways can be extremely complex. This is therefore a matter of intimate local knowledge and only an experienced senior pilot can offer advice concerning the handling of a ship in such specific locations.

It should also be borne in mind that a mass of water on the move is several hundred times denser than air and thus by comparison is capable of generating forces of enormous magnitude. In view of this, any attempt at simplifying the complicated formulae which are used to calculate tidal forces is unwise, as it can easily result in misleading and potentially dangerous under estimations. For a more detailed analysis of specific tidal problems and the forces involved it may be necessary to seek the advice of specialists in the field of hydrodynamics.

The effect of a tide upon a ship's handling characteristics
Fig. 34

The understandable belief that the tide will have an adverse effect upon the handling characteristics of a ship is to some extent a misconception. Provided a ship is clear of any external features which might obstruct the tide, such as shallow water, nearby shoals or man made structures, and no attempt is being made to restrict the tidal drift of the ship with tugs, anchors, or moorings, it can be handled in much same way as normal with no particular adverse effects (see figure 34).

The important difference lies in the fact that the area of water A/B/C/D, that encompasses a vessel's manoeuvre during any specific period of time, is moving en masse, together with the ship, throughout the duration of that manoeuvre. During this period, although the handling of the ship is not actually affected the ship is, relative to any fixed object such as a buoy or jetty, being carried away from the starting position of the intended movement. This can be quite a large distance. If for example, it takes 15 minutes to turn a ship short round in a 2 knot tide, the ship will have travelled $1/2$ a mile over the ground and down stream, during the course of that movement.

It is important, therefore, that the shiphandler assesses the tidal strength and direction with some care, prior to the commencement of any manoeuvre, in order to ascertain if there is sufficient time and space to complete it.

Working in a Tide

With the obvious exception of difficult and complex tidal situations, when the tide flows across a berth for example, it may often be found that the tide can be used to ......

- **improve slow speed control**.
- **create lateral motion**.

Fig. 34 Effect of Tide upon Ship Handling

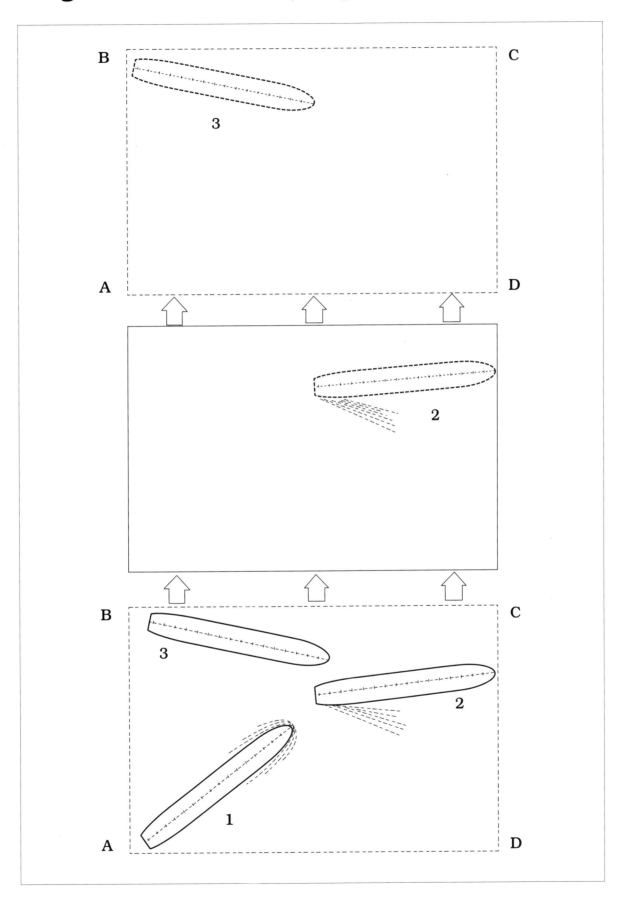

With the tide from ahead
Fig. 35(a)

By using low revolutions or short kicks ahead in order to maintain a small amount of headway 'through the water' and into the tide, it is possible to balance the ship's headway against the tide and keep the pivot point forward, even though the ship is making very little speed '**over the ground**'. This retains a good steering lever and positive control over the ship, but at a considerably lower speed over the ground than would otherwise be normal. In general terms this is known as '**stemming the tide**'.

Whilst stemming the tide in this manner it is helpful to keep an eye on the bearing of a fixed object on the beam, or even better a transit of two fixed objects on or near the beam, to enable the balance between headway and tide to be more carefully monitored. If the ship starts to fall back with the tide it may in fact be stopped in the water, this will move the pivot point back amidships and the ship's head will be less easy to control until headway through the water is resumed.

With the tide from astern
Fig. 35(b)

This is a most unsatisfactory situation and one where it is extremely difficult to maintain positive control of the ship. In this example, the ship is running with a 1·5 knot tide from astern. In order to maintain headway over the tide, or through the water and so keep the pivot point forward, the ship would have to be running at a speed over the ground which is considerably higher than the speed of the tide. This will often be far too fast!

To reduce the persistent high speed over the ground, it will be necessary to put the engines astern, perhaps frequently or for long periods of time and back the ship hard against the tide. Whilst doing this the pivot point will move aft and the ship is purely at the whim of transverse thrust.

It can be very difficult to keep control of a ship with a following tide. If practicable it is always preferable to stem the tide !

Working across a tide
Fig. 35(c) & (d)

If a reasonable balance has been achieved between the tidal stream and the ship's speed through the water, so that the ship's speed over the ground is minimal, it becomes possible to work the tide and create sideways or '**lateral motion**'. This can often be achieved by using rudder angle alone, but if that is not enough, a short kick ahead can be used to ease the tide around onto the appropriate bow. The resultant of the two vectors, tidal stream and ship's headway will then be noticeable, as the ship starts to work or 'crab' across the tide. To stop or correct this sideways drift, it will be necessary to bring the ship's head back around into the tide, so that it is once again dead ahead.

When using the tide in this way it is very important not to be impatient and put the tide too far around on the bow. This will create good lateral motion but if the angle of the tide upon the bow is too large, it may require too much time, power and clear distance ahead, to bring the ship's head back up into the tide. There may, for example, be insufficient water with which to do this in, particularly in the close proximity of a berth. It is therefore better to put the tide fine on the bow and then wait to see if it is having the desired effect, rather than rush the manoeuvre!

Fig. 35 Working in a Tide

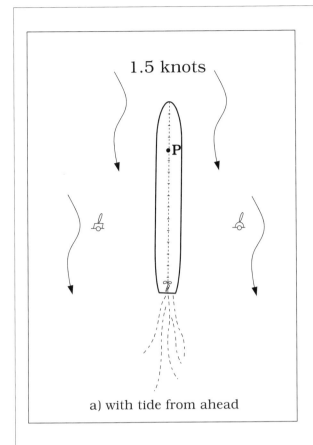

1.5 knots

•P

a) with tide from ahead

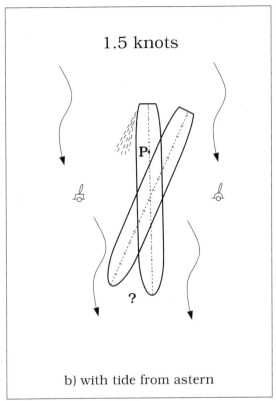

1.5 knots

P

?

b) with tide from astern

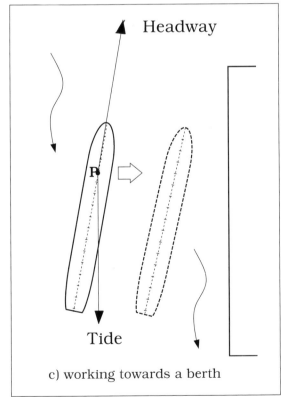

Headway

P

Tide

c) working towards a berth

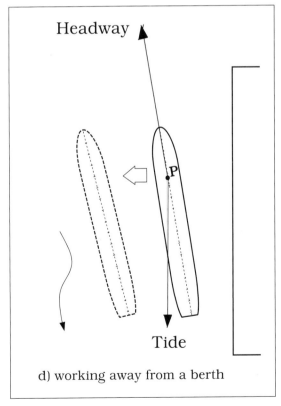

Headway

P

Tide

d) working away from a berth

By working the ship across a tidal stream in this manner, the tide is really being used as a sort of 'poor man's tug' and in tidal work, more than anywhere else, the ship handler needs to develop a keen, sensitive 'feel' for the movement of the ship, virtually drifting it into the desired position.

Swinging on an Anchor

From the foregoing it is clearly desirable to stem the tide for the majority of tidal operations, whenever that is possible. An inbound ship with a following flood tide, may therefore be faced with the need to 'swing' and turn through 180° to stem the tide prior to proceeding to its allocated berth.

In a wide, open waterway, with sufficient room down tide, it may be possible to turn a ship short round without the aid of anchors, or tugs. If however this has to be done in a narrow, restricted waterway, perhaps with limited space downstream, it will be necessary to keep a tight control over the ship's position at all times and this can only be achieved by swinging on an anchor. The art of **'swinging'** or turning on a tide to one anchor has been practised by masters and pilots in the coastal trades for many years past. Correctly done it makes an otherwise difficult and risky manoeuvre a relatively relaxed and easy one.

This manoeuvre can only be conducted if the river bed is clear of obstructions and this is a matter of local knowledge.

Fig. 36
Position 1

This manoeuvre, like all others, will obviously be open to individual interpretation and will depend, not only upon experience and skill of the ship handler, but also ......

- **the depth of water.**
- **under keel clearance.**
- **strength of current.**
- **type of bottom.**
- **type of engine power available.**
- **size of ship.**
- **amount of room available for turn.**

When working a ship into position, prior to letting go and swinging on an anchor, it may also be useful to consider the following points ......

- **plan to** conduct the swing in a direction that favours transverse thrust when going astern, if that it is practicable.
- endeavour to **get the speed down** to the minimum for steerage way, when approaching the swinging area.
- ensure there is **ample space** for the stern to swing around in during the turn.
- before letting go make certain that the **ship is canted the right way**, so that the tide is on the correct quarter to assist the turn.
- at the **instant of letting go, the speed over the ground should be as low as possible** and before the brake is applied the engines should already be going astern, to ease the weight on the windlass.

Fig. 36 Swinging to a Tide on One Anchor

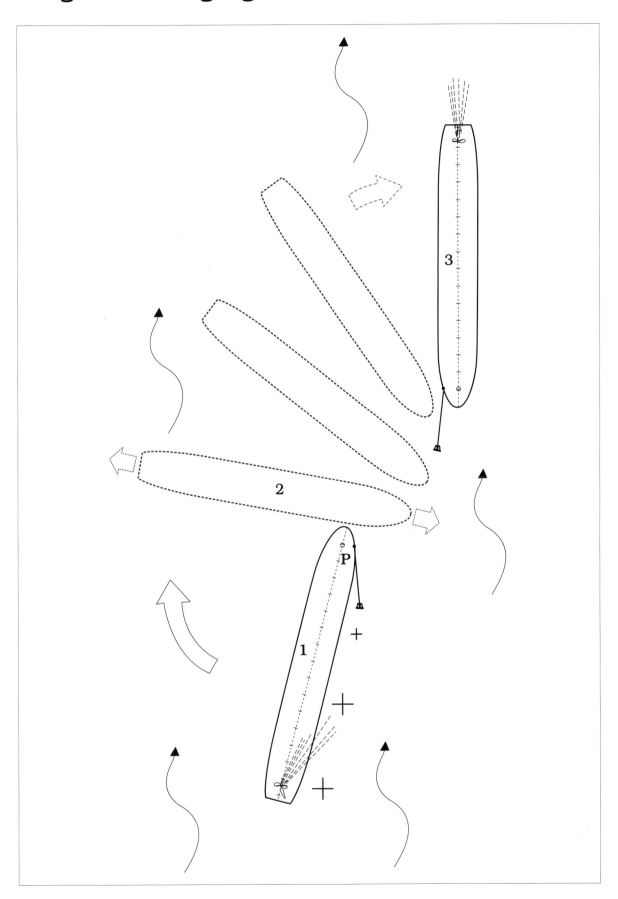

This is probably the most critical part of the manoeuvre and it is important to set this up correctly. Thereafter it all becomes much more relaxed.

Fig. 36
Position 2

Once the anchor is out and on the brake, even though it may not be holding, it should be sufficient to keep the pivot point right forward, so that the tide can work on a good turning lever and start to swing the ship around. However, if it doesn't feel as if it is working, it may be prudent to veer a little more cable. As the stern swings around, and it is usually surprisingly slowly, the main propulsion can be used either ahead or astern to ensure that the stern is swinging clear of any obstructions and that the ship is generally in a good position.

Fig. 36
Position 3

At some stage, it should be remembered that a lot of weight may be coming onto the windlass, as it takes the full weight of the ship on the tide! It is usually necessary to come ahead with the main propulsion and appropriate rudder i.e. kicks ahead, not only to assist the turn but also to ease the weight on the windlass.

Once the ship is stemming the tide, it is quite easy to keep control, while the windlass is put in gear and the anchor recovered, and then the vessel can proceed as required.

The amount of cable veered is very dependent upon depth, type of bottom and size of ship. For further information concerning the safety parameters when working anchors consult chapter 6.

Local Knowledge

Whilst the handling characteristics of a vessel are not actually affected by a tide, if a ship is in clear, undisturbed and relatively deep flowing water, the opposite is the case when a ship has to operate in or near an area where the tide is influenced by natural constraints and man made obstructions such as ......

- **bends in rivers**.
- **shoals**.
- **entrances to canals and rivers**.
- **moles, groynes and breakwaters**.
- **lock entrances and approaches**.
- **bridges**.
- **power station outlets**.
- **jetties**.
- **sea islands**.
- **large sbm's**.

There can be many areas throughout a tidal district where the tidal flow is complex and dangerous to the unwary. An unexpected change in the tidal conditions can have a rapid and devastating effect upon the handling of a ship.

Experienced pilots working in such areas develop specific skills based upon intimate local knowledge of their own district and this is an important part of the pilots job. The advice of these specialised pilots should always be sought and it is well beyond the scope of this publication to cover the multitude of complex tidal problems that exist within the many pilotage districts of the world. There may, however, be some value in looking at a few common examples.

Bends in a Tidal River

The bends in a tidal river are a good example of areas where the tide may be of differing strengths, perhaps running very rapidly on the outside of the bend but relatively weaker on the inside of the bend.

With a following tide
Fig. 37(a)

If a relatively large ship is rounding a bend in a channel, with a strong following tide, it is possible for the ship to be positioned so that the strong tide is working on the after body of the ship, whilst only the weaker tide is influencing the fore body. With the pivot point forward the strongest tide is thus working on a good turning lever and a turning force of considerable magnitude is created.

A ship can react both violently and rapidly to this force and it should never be underestimated !

Whilst it may be anticipated and corrected with a kick ahead of full power, sometimes this will not be sufficient to counteract the large force involved and the ship will continue to swing around, with a serious possibility of subsequently going aground.

Assuming there is a choice, it may be prudent to keep to the outside of the bend, so that the ship is always in the area of stronger flowing tide. If it is necessary to put the stern into a strong following tide, it should only be done with extreme caution!

With a tide from ahead
Fig. 37(b)

When a ship, again relatively large, is negotiating a bend in a channel, this time with the tide from ahead, it is also possible to get into a position where the ship is influenced by tides of differing strength. In this example it is the ship's bow that is now influenced by the very strong tide while the after body of the ship is in the area of relatively weaker tide. This creates a turning moment which is opposing the intended turn and if it is not anticipated with appropriate helm and power, it can surprise the unwary and the vessel may not come around in sufficient time to clear the bend, without the risk of grounding.

If it is practicable it is better to keep to the inside of a bend, so that the bow does not enter the area of stronger tide at any time during the turn. Unfortunately this is often the shallow side of the bend as well and this may be prohibitive to a larger vessel with a draft restraint.

Rapid changes in tidal direction
Fig. 38(a)

There are occasions when a ship is required to pass close to shallow areas or man made structures, where the tide may change rapidly in direction over a very short distance. If a ship is proceeding at slow speed this can have a very serious consequences for the handling of that vessel.

In the example in figure 38a, a ship is passing close to the end of a jetty and an area of shallow water, with the ship's head already canted to starboard to allow for the set and drift of the tide. As the shoal comes abeam the ship suddenly loses the influence of the tide forward, but

Fig. 37 Bends in a Tidal River

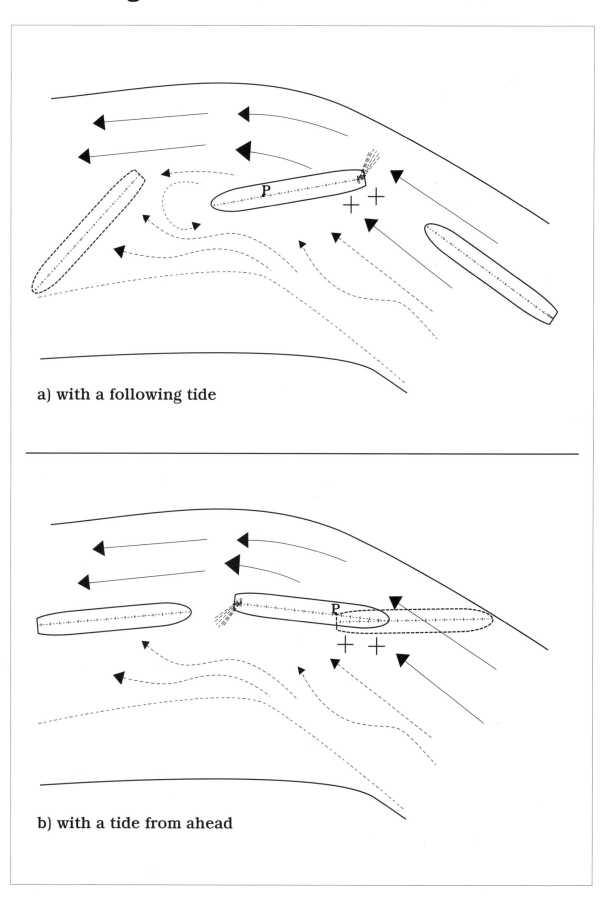

a) with a following tide

b) with a tide from ahead

Fig. 38 Local Tidal Anomalies

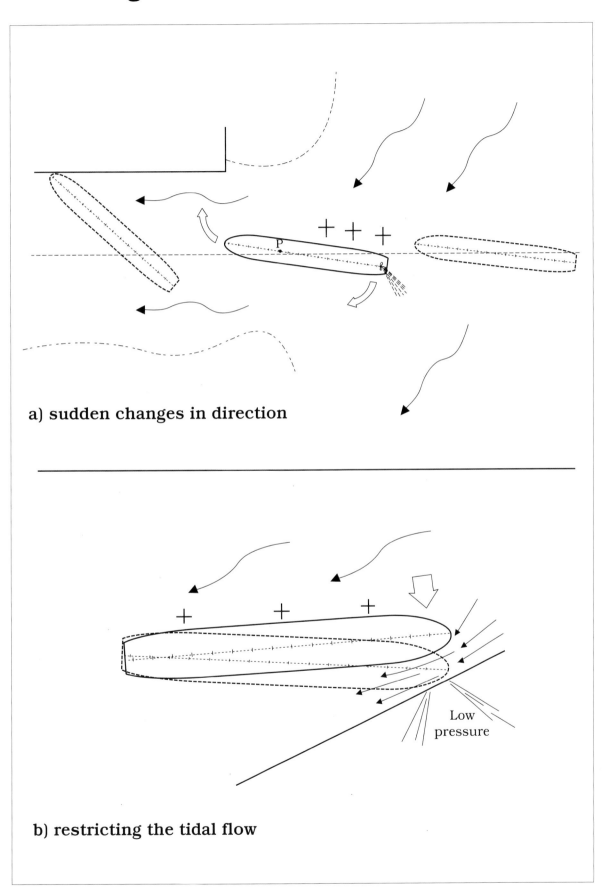

a) sudden changes in direction

b) restricting the tidal flow

it is still working strongly on the starboard quarter. With the combination of slow speed and the pivot point forward, the tide aft is working on a good turning lever. This creates a strong turning moment and the bow, which was already canted that way, will swing rapidly to starboard. It is therefore important to anticipate this and check it immediately, with a substantial kick ahead.

Equally important, as the ship comes out of the tide, the fact is that the ship may swing just as quickly to port, unless the corrective helm and power is promptly taken off. It is not unknown for this chain of events, particularly with strong cross tides, to generate into a situation where a large ship can swing rapidly out of control, from one side of the channel to the other and eventually aground!

Restricting the tidal flow
Fig. 38(b)

This is an unusual tidal problem but one that can, nevertheless, cause a considerable amount of damage to a jetty, if the ship in question is very large. It occurs when a ship is angled in towards a jetty and diagonally across a tide (see figure 38b).

With the ship blocking the tide, even though it may be quite weak, the tide is forced to flow with increased velocity between the ship and the jetty, thus creating a low pressure area between the two. The ship, surprisingly perhaps, can be sucked into and accelerated towards this area, with the risk of damage to both the ship and the quay. It is advisable therefore, to avoid acute angles with a jetty, even in fairly weak tides.

Interestingly, in a case which occurred some years ago, a VLCC was involved in a serious incident which resulted in major damage to an oil terminal, partly as a result of this phenomena. In an attempt to stop the ship's bow landing heavily on the jetty, two tugs in attendance forward dug in with full power. Instead of lifting the vessel off, it continued to run into the jetty with devastating results. Subsequent trials showed that the tugs combined propeller wash, running around the bow between the ship and the jetty, had created a low pressure area which the ship had accelerated into.

(It is interesting to note that the low pressure area created in these examples, by a ship that is virtually stopped in the water, is very similar to the bank effect illustrated in chapter 7 — Interaction, by a ship making way through the water.)

Tidal Forces
General

The force of the tide can be immense. Water is several hundred times denser than air and if any attempt is made to restrict its flow by holding the ship with moorings, anchors or tugs it can generate an enormous force. The magnitude of this force is influenced by ......

- **draft and depth of water**.
- **the ship's bow configuration**.
- **the velocity of the tide**.
- **under keel clearance**.

Depth and Draft

When it is required to calculate the force of the tide accurately, the draft and depth of water are important factors, particularly in the case of a large vessel such as a VLCC, because the velocity of the tides can vary substantially with depth. It is important to be aware that published 'tidal stream' information may only be based upon data recorded at limited depths. A tidal difference of up to 2·5 knots over a depth of 4·5 metres has been recorded in the past.

In the absence of reliable tidal information any calculations which ascertain the strength of the tide may be very inaccurate.

Bow configuration

Whilst not vital to a basic understanding of tidal forces, it is interesting to note that the shape of a ship's bow has a significant effect upon tidal force. The difference between the modern conventional bulbous bow and the more traditional rounded bow, has to be taken into account when the interests of accuracy are paramount. This is essential, for example, when calculating the current loads of a particular class of ship, in order to determine the mooring parameters at specific terminals.

Velocity of the tide

The force of the tide upon a ship, measured in tonnes, is directly proportional to the square of the velocity of the tide.

This means that for even a small increase in the velocity of the tide, there is an enormous increase in the force exerted upon a ship.

Under keel clearance

The single greatest influence upon the magnitude of the tidal force is under keel clearance.

This is due to the blocking effect of a vessel as the under keel clearance is reduced, so that the tide cannot flow under the vessel and is forced to flow around the ship. The ratio of the vessel's draft to the depth of water is therefore important.

With a depth to draft ratio of 1·05 the tidal force is three times stronger than with a depth to draft ratio of 3·0.

The tidal force at anchor
Fig. 39(a) and (b)
Fig. 40

A ship at anchor on a falling tide is an excellent example with which to illustrate the relationship between under keel clearance and the force of the tide. In this particular illustration the ship is a 50,000 dwt tanker lying to an anchor in a 5 knot tide. Initially the ship has a depth to draft ratio of 3·0 and the tide is free to flow around and under the hull, exerting a longitudinal tidal force of **19 tonnes** upon the ship and through the windlass (see figure 39a).

If the under keel clearance is slowly reduced by a falling tide, for example, until the depth to draft ratio is 1·1 it will progressively restrict the flow of water under the hull and slowly increase the tidal force upon the ship. In this case it is increased by approximately three times the original figure, to **64 tonnes** (see figure 39b).

Fig. 39 Tidal Force at Anchor

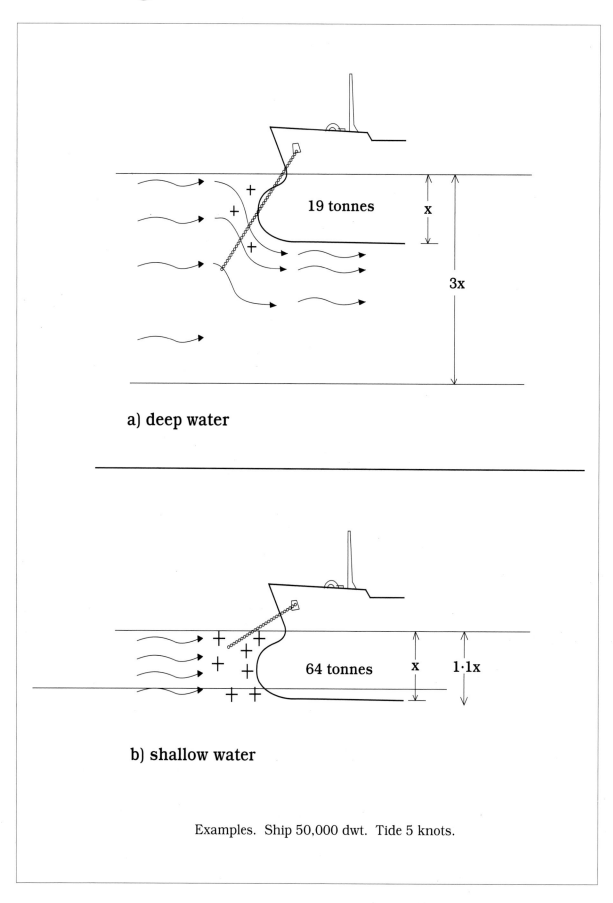

a) deep water

b) shallow water

Examples. Ship 50,000 dwt. Tide 5 knots.

This is an extremely important point, because the force of a strong tide over the period of dead low water could just exceed the holding power of the anchor and the ship will drag, particularly if the ship is laying to a strong wind as well!

An example of these forces is illustrated in the table (figure 40).

Lateral tidal forces Fig. 41(a) and (b)

The cross sectional area of a hull that is exposed to a tide when a ship is at anchor is relatively small in comparison to the area which is exposed to the tide, when a ship is either moored, or held with the tide on the beam. If, in addition, the ship has a small under keel clearance, so that the tide is prohibited from flowing underneath the hull and for the full length of the ship is forced to pass around the bow and stern, the lateral force created can be enormous (see figure 41a).

This is best illustrated with an example, which in this case is based upon a series of calculations and tank tests for a ship of 280,000 dwt. The ship is loaded with a draft of 22 metres, is laying with a 1 knot tide on the beam and has a depth to draft ratio of 1·05.

As a result of these calculations it is evident that this particular ship will experience a lateral force of **328 tonnes** on the beam in those circumstances.

Due to the differing underwater profile of the bow and stern, this has also been calculated to show that the forces at the forward and aft perpendiculars were 153 and 175 tonnes respectively (see figure 41b).

The force of the tide varies in direct proportion to the square of the tidal velocity, therefore an increase in tidal velocity of 0·5 knots to 1·5 knots will increase the lateral force in this example to over **700 tonnes**!

Bearing this in mind, it is essential to remember that a small increase in the velocity of the tide can place enormous current loads on a ship with a small under keel clearance. On the beam this force might easily exceed the bollard pull of a tug and great care needs to taken before placing a ship, with a small under keel clearance, across a beam tide. This is particularly important within the confines of a river, where in addition the ship might also be blocking the tidal flow of that river.

There have been cases in the past, throughout several pilotage districts, where this has resulted in both unexpected and exceptionally difficult handling problems. Often, with hindsight, it has been necessary to consider a more suitable tidal window, in order to obtain better tidal conditions, particularly in respect of under keel clearances.

Thus far, in the interests of simplicity, the tide has only be considered as a separate lateral or longitudinal force, either on the beam or dead ahead. It may of course be x° on the bow and it should be pointed out that the appropriate calculations do take this into account. The tide can be broken down into its individual components of yaw, or turning moment, and a combination of both lateral and longitudinal forces. This is a specialised field of expertise, involving the use of complex graphs and mathematical equations. For those wishing to pursue this subject in greater depth, the appropriate source of reference is given in the bibliography at the end this publication.

Fig. 40 Longitudinal Forces on a Tanker with a 50 knot wind and a 5 knot tide in a sheltered anchorage

Tanker dead-weight tonnes	Depth to draught ratio	Forces acting on the bow			Anchor holding power tonnes
		Wind tonnes	Current tonnes	Total tonnes	
50,802	3.0	20.05	18.79	38.84	60.9
	2.0	"	30.56	50.61	
	1.4	"	47.54	67.59	
	1.2	"	56.58	76.63	
	1.1	"	63.37	83.42	
101,605	3.0	22.96	27.00	49.96	90.3
	2.0	"	43.92	66.88	
	1.4	"	68.32	91.28	
	1.2	"	81.32	104.28	
	1.1	"	91.07	114.03	
152,407	3.0	23.42	34.33	57.75	112.7
	2.0	"	55.85	79.27	
	1.4	"	86.87	110.29	
	1.2	"	103.44	126.86	
	1.1	"	115.86	139.28	
203,209	3.0	23.87	39.90	63.77	131.6
	2.0	"	64.90	88.77	
	1.4	"	100.95	124.82	
	1.2	"	120.18	144.05	
	1.1	"	134.60	158.47	
254,012	3.0	24.33	45.56	69.89	150.5
	2.0	"	74.10	98.43	
	1.4	"	115.26	139.59	
	1.2	"	137.22	161.55	
	1.1	"	153.67	178.00	
304,814	3.0	24.78	53.56	78.34	171.5
	2.0	"	87.11	111.89	
	1.4	"	135.51	160.29	
	1.2	"	161.33	186.11	
	1.1	"	180.69	205.47	

Fig. 41 Lateral Tidal Forces

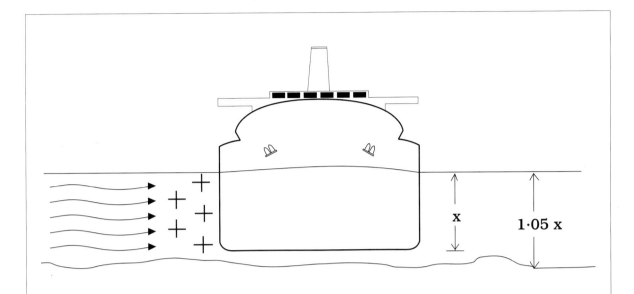

a) blocking the tidal flow

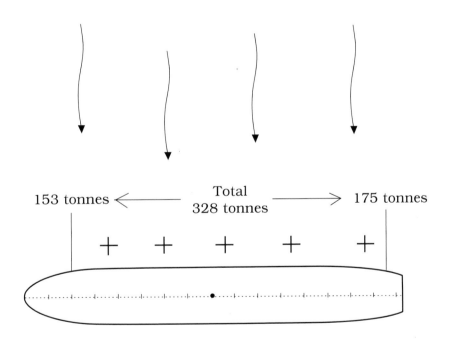

153 tonnes ← Total 328 tonnes → 175 tonnes

b) the resultant forces

Example: Ship 280,000 dwt. Tide 1 knot

**Running lines ashore after a successful stern berthing
using tugs and thruster combined**

CHAPTER NINE

BOW THRUSTER WORK

Introduction

IT IS NOT UNCOMMON for the masters and officers of ferries, cruise ships, supply boats and other similar vessels, to spend a high proportion of their operational service in a busy manoeuvring environment. There, in a relatively short period of time, they can gain a considerable amount of shiphandling experience on ships which are usually fitted with twin propellers and bow thruster(s) and are therefore considered fairly 'handy'. This area of bow thruster work is not the concern of this chapter.

The single screw ship, such as a container ship, car carrier, tanker or bulk carrier, no matter what its size, does however represent an altogether different case. These vessels are usually engaged on long haul trades which afford infrequent opportunities to gain a great deal of experience in 'hands on' ship handling and although some ships are fitted with bow thrusters, to improve their handling characteristics, they are none the less single screw vessels which can still be comparatively difficult to handle and relatively unforgiving.

The objective of this chapter is, therefore, to discuss some of the more important points that should be kept in mind when using a bow thruster to assist in the handling of a single screw ship.

Reliability

In the past, and to some extent to this day, pilots are often, quite correctly, distrustful of bow thrusters. This is in part due to their poor track record for reliability. There is no doubt that older units with outdated electrics or hydraulics are prone to problems, situated as they are somewhat remotely, deep down in the fore part of the ship and subjected to the pounding of heavy weather, vibration and damp, in a truly hostile environment, compounded by lack of use and neglect on long sea passages.

Fortunately the demand for reliable bow thrusters in super ferries, exploration work and other specialised fields, coupled with modern technology, has led to the development of altogether more robust and reliable units. These can be used in all manner of vessels from large tankers to tugs, although of course a pilot must still keep a wary eye open for poor maintenance and neglect.

More importantly, and again with some justification many pilots may still appear to be quite sceptical concerning bow thrusters mainly because they are all too often underpowered and therefore perceived as inadequate.

Power
Fig. 42

There is a variety of bow thruster units in use today, which range from the unusual, a V10 diesel engine on the forecastle with an amazing 30m drive shaft on a VLCC, to the more common, a reversible electric motor in principle not unlike a cargo winch, driving a fixed pitch propeller, or an electric motor with a hydraulically operated variable pitch propeller. On many vessels the design parameters are severely limited by the need to place the drive units in

Fig. 42 Graph of Wind Speed
& Thruster Force

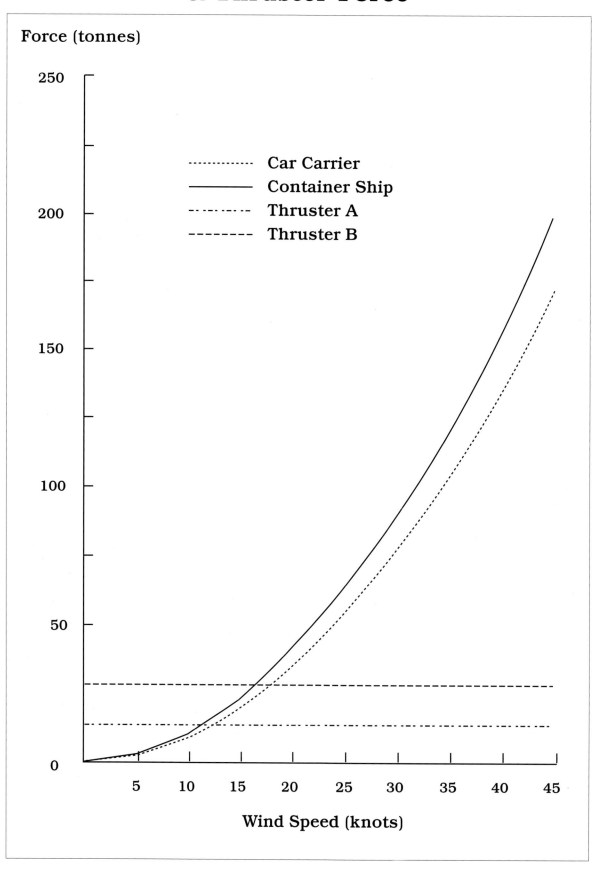

Force (tonnes)

Wind Speed (knots)

a restricted location, low down in the narrow fore part of the ship. Even if more space is available on a larger ship, the size of tunnel and therefore propeller is still restricted by practical considerations such as the ballast draft, integral hull strength and realistic maintenance levels.

This limitation of power due to the imposition of tunnel size is particularly evident on large super ferries where, despite increasingly large tonnages, it is still necessary, due to operational restrictions, to retain a relatively shallow draft. In these circumstances it is common to see such vessels fitted with twin bow thrusters in order to improve power output. Similarly, in other trades, there are one or two single screw ships that enjoy the benefits of improved bow thruster design. Unfortunately this is not generally the case and on many vessels power output may be disappointing.

The rating, or power, of a bow thruster is often given in kilowatts (kW). This may be confusing to the inexperienced and it makes it difficult to compare thruster power to another force such as a tug or the wind. To improve this situation an approximate conversion can be made to either shaft horse power (shp) or tonnes (t) force given that ......

- 0·74 kW = 1 shp
- 100 shp = 1 t

A common range of thrusters would therefore give the following............

•	500 kW	676 shp	6 t
•	750 kW	1014 shp	10 t
•	1000 kW	1351 shp	13 t
•	1250 kW	1689 shp	17 t
•	1500 kW	2027 shp	20 t
•	1750 kW	2364 shp	24 t
•	2000 kW	2702 shp	27 t

Looking at this list it should be remembered that thrusters, rather like tugs, may sometimes have a slightly better conversion from kilowatts to shaft horse power. This may be due to design improvements in propeller characteristics, the fairing and ducting of tunnel apertures or anything else that will improve the rate of water flow through the tunnel without increasing motor size.

It is now possible to compare thruster force to wind force, using a car carrier of 198m and a container ship of 210m as examples. The wind force on the beam for each ship is illustrated by a simple graph in figure 42 and shows a quadratic curve indicating a rapid increase in tonnes force for relatively small increases in wind speed, most noticeably with the higher wind strengths. In order to compare this with a broad range of thruster power two bow thrusters of 1000kW and 2000kW are shown with straight dotted lines across the graph at 13 and 27 tonnes respectively.

In the case of the container ship the wind load force exceeds thruster force at ......

- 1000kW   11kts (Force 3/4)
- 2000kW   16kts (Force 4/5)

and on the car carrier it is at ......

- 1000kW   13kts (Force 4)
- 2000kW   18kts (Force 5)

This it should be noted, is the maximum wind strength, so should it become either necessary or prudent to make an allowance for gusty conditions, the result will be a relatively poor range indeed. Thus the weather window will need to be watched most carefully to avoid being caught with insufficient resources. These examples are only shown in order to give some general indication as to the possible limitations that might be encountered. Individual experience of specific ships may naturally be much better or indeed far worse.

Whilst it would appear that little imagination or thought is required to thrust the bow hither and thither, as seemingly required, there are one or two specific aspects of bow thruster work which are worth looking into more closely. These are ......

- **thrusting when stopped**.
- **the thruster and headway**.
- **creating lateral motion**.
- **working the thruster with sternway**.

This may help to encourage more confidence in those not familiar with bow thruster work.

Thrusting when stopped

The simple process of thrusting the bow to port or starboard, whilst the ship is stopped, may not initially appear to warrant much concern. Once, however, the ship is being worked close to a jetty, other vessels or any obstruction, where movement and positioning need to be carefully monitored, there are two aspects which may occasionally be of some significance ......

- **position of the pivot point**.
- **unexpected movement ahead**.

Position of pivot point
Fig. 43(a)

When a ship is stopped and the bow thruster is activated, to thrust the bow in the desired direction, it is (due to the underwater profile of the ship) working on a pivot point which is located well aft and in a position which is roughly the equivalent of one ship's beam from the stern (see figure 43a). If the thruster is of a modest 10 tonnes bollard pull this will give it a turning moment of ......

10t x 145m = 1450tm

This is probably the best turning moment that can be achieved because any subsequent headway, or sternway, will move the pivot point adversely and shorten the turning lever accordingly. This will be illustrated in this chapter.

Fig. 43 Thrusting when Stopped

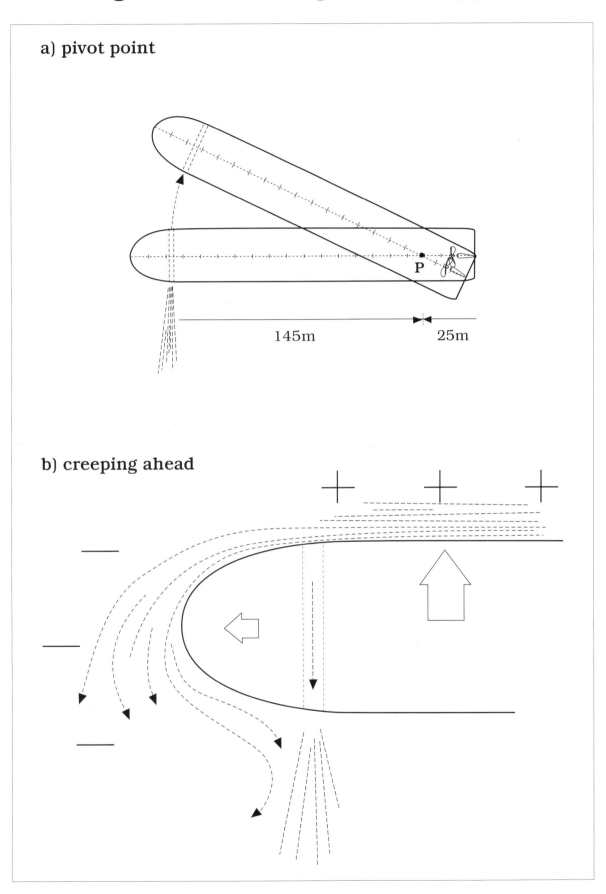

a) pivot point

145m   25m

b) creeping ahead

Fig. 44 Thrusting with Headway

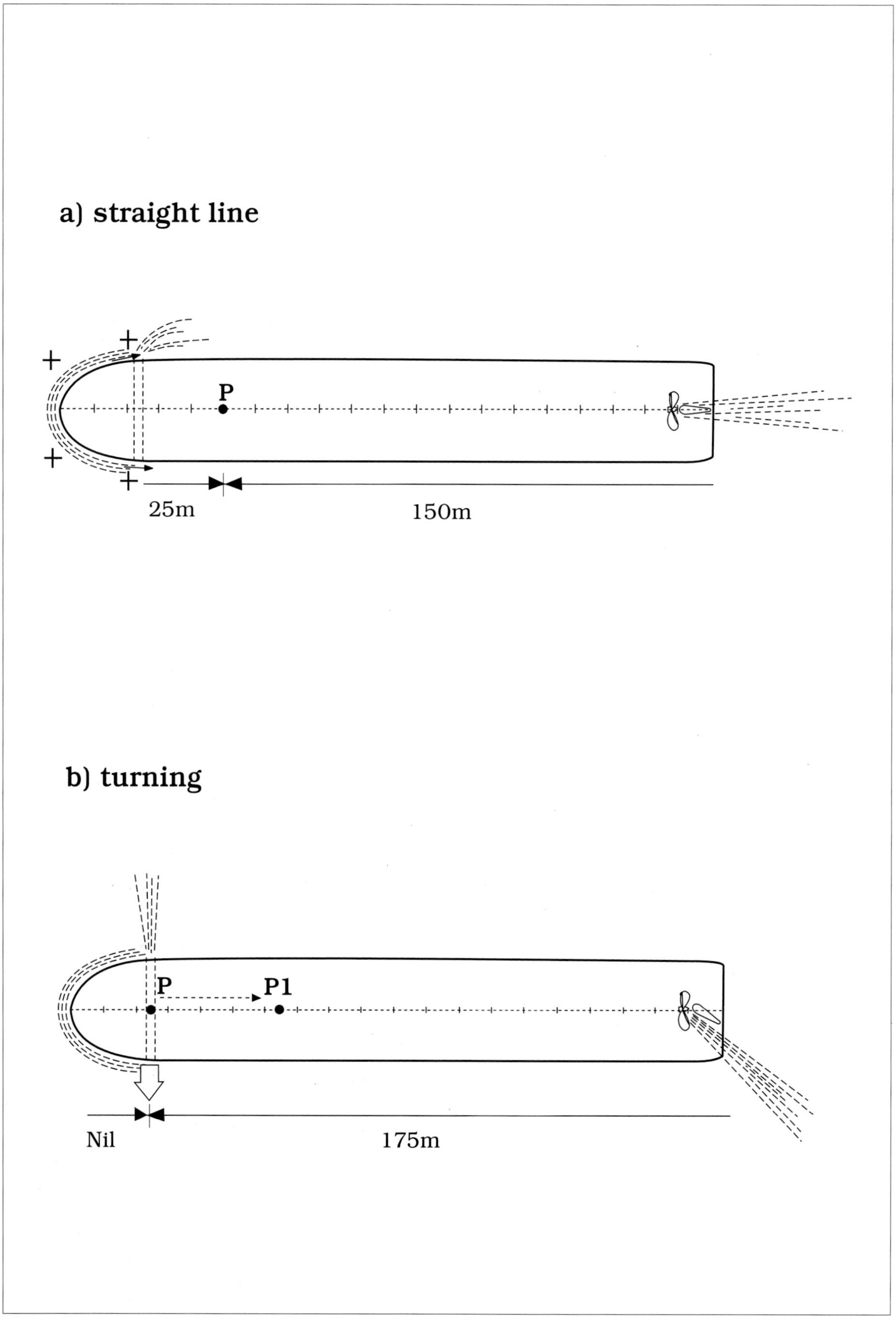

a) straight line

25m   150m

b) turning

Nil   175m

Unexpected movement ahead
Fig. 43(b)

It is not uncommon for some officers to have noticed that a ship appears to develop a small amount of headway, seemingly as a result of using its bow thruster. This is most noticeable when the ship was previously stopped in the water. This phenomenon may partially be initiated by a build up of positive water pressure along the ship's side, as it is thrust sideways by the thruster (see figure 43b). This in turn creates a flow of water around the bow which may be of sufficient velocity to create a low pressure area immediately ahead of the ship.

In addition to this, it is thought likely that the bow thruster draws in water more easily from the bow area, rather than from aft of the tunnel and this will also encourage the development of a low pressure around the bow. In a similar manner to interaction and bank effect the ship will tend to 'sniff or smell' this area and creep ahead, particularly if the bow thruster is operated, perhaps a little too often or a little too vigorously.

Thrusting with Headway
Fig. 44(a) and (b)

When using a bow thruster while a ship is making headway, the first limitation is that which is imposed by too high a speed. With the exception of a few powerful units and multi-thruster units, performance will fall off quite rapidly once the ship's speed has risen above 2 knots or thereabouts. At higher speeds, turbulence will develop at the tunnel entrances, spreading through the tunnel to seriously impair propeller performance. Externally, the increasing water flow across the tunnel mouth soon deflects the meagre thruster output. In an attempt towards improving this, some manufacturers have altered the shape of the tunnel apertures, thus improving water flow through the tunnel, but despite this, excessive speed will probably still be detrimental to thruster efficiency.

Less obvious, but much more important, is the position of the ship's pivot point which, when the vessel is making headway but not turning, is approximately $1/4$ of the ship's length from the bow (see figure 44a). This has the effect of placing the thruster on a very short turning lever, in this case 25m, and the resultant turning moment is poor ......

10t x 25m = 250tm

This illustrates the main reason for a reduction in the thruster's turning ability as the ship gathers headway, in comparison with the previous example, when the ship was stopped. When a ship commences to make headway but is also turning, as with a standing turn or a kick ahead at very low speeds, the effect upon the thruster needs to be considered separately, because the pivot point behaves slightly differently. With full rudder applied, as the vessel begins to make headway, the pivot point moves to a position well forward, approximately $1/8$ of the ship's length from the bow (see figure 44b).

This unfortunately coincides very closely with the position of the bow thruster which, for a brief period, will be working right on the pivot point with virtually no turning lever and therefore a poor if not negligible turning moment. The unwary eye looking forward may still feel that the bow is turning when in fact it is actually being pushed sideways.

If the ship continues to turn with the power on, the speed will naturally increase and the pivot point will be pushed back to a position roughly $^1/_3$ of the ship's length from forward. Whilst this may improve the turning lever slightly, unfortunately any advantage will quickly be eradicated by the adverse effect of increasing speed. Whilst a thruster may often 'appear' very useful for controlling heading when making headway at low speeds, it is clearly not very efficient at this task as it is always working too close to the pivot point. It is on the other hand extremely useful, if used in conjunction with the ship's main propulsion, at developing sideways movement or 'lateral motion'.

Lateral Motion to Port

An ability, instinctively, to feel lateral movement in a ship is a very important part of good shiphandling and driving a ship by 'the seat of the pants.' It is also, of course, possible to develop lateral motion intentionally, with the judicious use of kicks ahead. This is frequently put to good effect when working a vessel up to a berth. If a bow thruster is available as well it can be used simultaneously with kicks ahead to generate even better lateral motion, particularly on the bigger class of ship where the kinetic energy of such a large vessel moving sideways can carry on for quite some time. It is, however, very important to appreciate that there is a considerable difference between trying to work a single screw ship to port, as opposed to starboard. This will be illustrated in the following examples.

It is assumed, throughout the following, that the ship has a right-handed propeller when making headway. If required it should be relatively easy to review the examples for ship's with left-handed propellers and either fixed or variable pitch.

Fig. 45
Position 1

Lateral motion to port can be initiated with good but short kicks ahead on full starboard rudder, in conjunction with a balanced amount of thrust to port on the bow thruster. This will also kill any undesirable swing of the bow to starboard. The question of balancing the thruster power against a kick ahead is not always easy and a comparison of thruster and kick ahead power range may be useful as a rough guide. In an example with a ship of 200m length we might find the following ......

- **Thruster**   **1351shp**   **13t**
- Main Engine   12,000shp   120t

A kick ahead with full power might realistically only produce some 40 or 50% of main engine power in terms of side thrust, in this case approximately 48 to 60 tonnes, and this can be apportioned according to the rpm.

- **Dead Slow Ahead**   **13t**
- Slow Ahead   27t
- Half Ahead   40t
- Full Ahead   54t

Although this is only the most crude of comparisons, even allowing for a considerable percentage of inaccuracy, it still is sufficient to show that ......

- full bow thrust of 13t is only equal to a kick ahead of dead slow.
- a kick ahead with full power is 54t and actually very powerful.

Fig. 45 Lateral Motion to Port

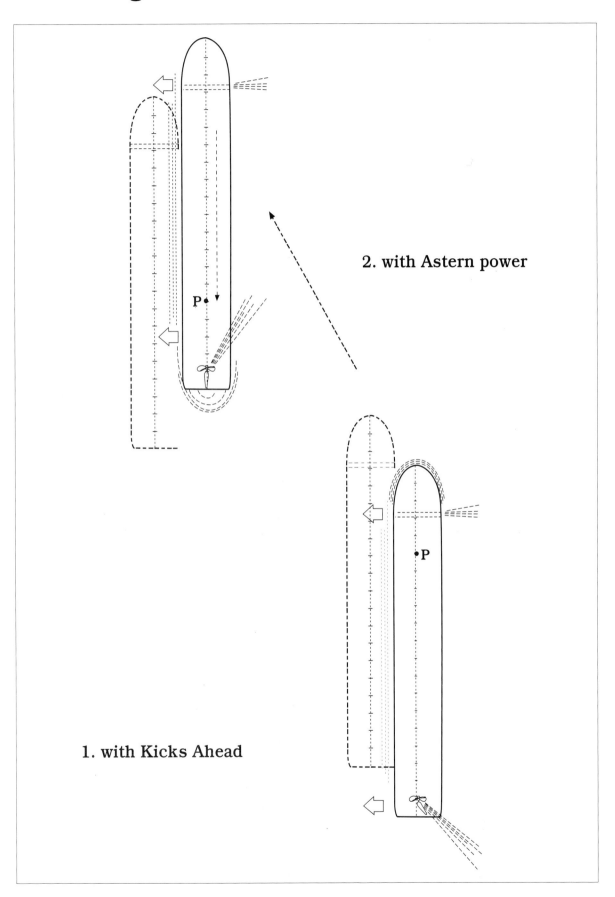

2. with Astern power

1. with Kicks Ahead

Another consideration, particularly on ships with controllable pitch propellers, is that the reaction of a thruster may be much slower than the main propeller and therefore it sometimes needs to be brought in a little earlier than the kick ahead. It is not the intention of the foregoing to imply that only dead slow ahead should be used. On the contrary, more powerful kicks ahead may frequently be needed. With these points in mind, however, it may be possible to find something of a compromise between thruster and kick ahead.

Figure 45
Position 2

When the propeller is put astern, more often than not to reduce the headway which has built up as a result of kicks ahead, the transverse thrust of the propeller on the starboard quarter will continue to thrust the stern to port and the anticipated kick around of the bow to starboard can be stopped by applying port bow thrust. The combination of these two forces will maintain the lateral motion previously generated with kicks ahead, thus making it a relatively easy task to work the ship to port as it will appear to have a natural tendency to do so. This can be very effective with large tonnage ships, even to the extent that some caution may be required to avoid landing too fast and too heavily.

Lateral motion to Starboard

In comparison with working a single screw ship to port, this is much more problematic and experience has shown that having a bow thruster does not allow any relaxation of forethought to the approach and positioning of the ship when attempting to work a vessel to starboard. It can go very badly wrong!

Figure 46
Position 1

At this stage there is no apparent problem and in much the same manner as the previous example, when working to port, a combination of kicks ahead with well balanced thruster work will generate lateral motion to starboard.

Figure 46
Position 2

The problem begins when astern power is applied, usually to control headway. As a result, the bow is likely to swing inexorably to starboard and there is then a natural tendency, automatically to apply port bow thrust to check it. This combination of transverse thrust aft, pushing the stern to port and the bow being thrust to port forward, results in an insidious and altogether unintentional creation of lateral motion to port which, if too much power is used, can be of sufficient magnitude to take the ship back out to where it was in the first place and perhaps even beyond. It is extremely embarrassing to see every effort to work the ship to starboard, thwarted by an inexplicable and relentless drift to port, in the opposite direction! Every care should be taken to avoid placing a ship into a position which creates the need to work it to starboard unnecessarily. This can be achieved by keeping the approach fine and close whenever possible, but above all by keeping stern power to a minimum thus avoiding prolonged and excessive periods with the propeller running astern.

Thrusting with Sternway
Fig. 47(a) and (b)

Apart from when a ship is stopped it is only when making sternway, with or without the main propulsion working astern, that a bow thruster really proves its worth and becomes relatively efficient. This is because the pivot

Fig. 46 Lateral Motion to Starboard

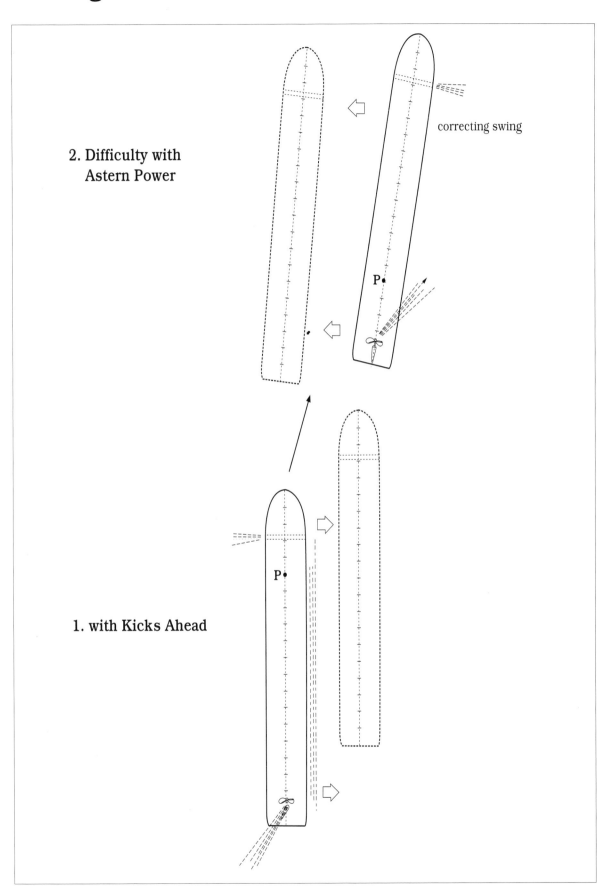

2. Difficulty with
   Astern Power

correcting swing

P

1. with Kicks Ahead

P

Fig. 47 Thrusting with Sternway

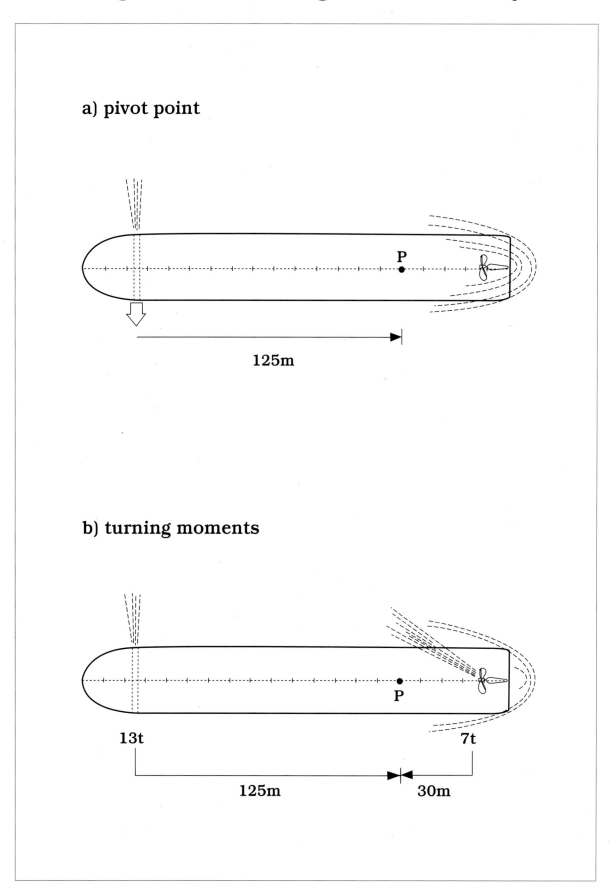

a) pivot point

125m

b) turning moments

13t

125m   30m   7t

point has moved aft to a position approximately a $^1/_4$ of the ships length from the stern (see figure 47a) and the bow thruster can now work on a respectable turning lever, in this case 125m.

The thruster can be used to steer the ship very effectively, as it makes sternway, in much the same manner as a rudder and, although it doesn't take long to get the feel of it, one or two points are worth keeping in mind ......

- the thruster may be slow coming up to full power.
- the ship will steer quite sluggishly with a tendency to 'flop' either side of the intended heading if permitted to do so.
- the thruster will be slow correcting any large rate of turn.
- looking astern from a bridge aft, the eye does not perceive rate of turn as quickly as it would when looking forward to the bow.

To the unwary, the key elements which may create problems are the sluggish nature of the response times and poor thruster power. Whilst the latter cannot be avoided, it is possible to avoid the former by watching the heading and rate of turn with absolute total concentration. It is unwise to let the ship wander too far of off the intended track, or allow too big a rate of turn to develop. If it does it should be hit quickly with a 'bold and vigorous' use of the appropriate thruster power. At some stage it is going to be imperative to use stern power, perhaps to get or keep the ship moving astern. This then brings in the need to consider the additional effect of transverse thrust during periods when the main propulsion is used astern in conjunction with a bow thruster.

To do this it is advantageous to have some idea as to how much force in tonnes is actually being exerted on the quarter by the transverse thrust. Using the same ship of 200m with a 12,000shp main engine, and assuming for the sake of this example that the stern power is only equivalent to 60% of the ahead power, then the main propulsion when running astern will only be generating some 7,200shp. This is the maximum output, and it is quite possible that as little as 10% of this total stern power will be trained onto the hull as transverse thrust, in which case this ship will have a transverse force at full astern of only ......

- 720 shp or **7 tonnes**

While there is no doubt that stern power, hull design and therefore transverse thrust may vary from ship to ship, it still remains in general terms a relatively poor force. This is compounded by the fact that when the ship is making sternway, it is also working too close to the pivot point and consequently upon a very poor turning lever, (see figure 47b) which in this illustration may be as small as 30m. If this is now compared to the bow thruster of **13 tonnes**, the maximum turning moments are ......

Transverse Thrust	7t	x 30m	=	210tm
Bow Thruster	13t	x125m	=	1625tm

It should, therefore, provided the conditions are favourable, be possible to work the ship astern by overriding the effect of transverse thrust with the bow thruster. This is indeed very effective. For this reason it may often be preferred, in the case of ships fitted with a bow thruster, to back up a waterway or to a berth.

Working Astern in a Channel
Fig. 48

The process of backing a ship up a waterway with the aid of a bow thruster is a very rewarding and satisfying operation which many officers take to quite quickly. Past observation, however, has shown that the inexperienced can often, unintentionally, allow a ship to become a victim of the insidious and therefore unexpected influence of lateral motion and can eventually end up with the ship in a difficult and occasionally irretrievable situation. This is illustrated in figure 48 with a ship in the following sequence of positions.

Fig. 48
Position 1

The ship at this stage has just entered the channel, is in a good position and the bow is canted to port to allow for a prolonged use of stern power while stern way is built up.

Fig. 48
Position 2

In this position the transverse thrust has either been corrected too late or not at all and the stern has been allowed to drop away from the centre of the channel. If the bow thruster is now applied to correct this, while the main engine is still going astern, for a short period the ship will be under the influence of both transverse thrust and bow thrust which combine to generate lateral motion to port. This is not intentional and may not actually be noticed initially.

Fig. 48
Position 3

Here the ship is steady on the correct heading, but that little bit of lateral movement has positioned the ship slightly off the centre line. Although this is not always seen as a problem at this stage, it might be more advantageous to use the bow thruster vigorously and steer the stern back to the centre of the channel, particularly as the propeller is still working astern and encouraging an unwanted trend to port.

Fig. 48
Position 4

It may now be the case that the sequence of events in position 2 is repeated once, or even twice, and each time the combination of thruster and transverse thrust ensures that the ship maintains its inexorable drift towards the edge of the channel. This can be more pronounced on a vessel of large tonnage, where the kinetic energy developed in moving it sideways can keep it drifting that way for some time, especially when encouraged to do so at frequent intervals. A light wind on the starboard side will augment and help to keep this tendency going remarkably well.

Fig. 48
Position 5

The ship could eventually be getting too close to the edge of the channel, to the extent that it is running out of manoeuvring space and although it is necessary to lift the stern back out into the channel, this is not possible because there is insufficient water to enable the bow to be thrusted to port.

Fig. 48
Position 6

Having lost the space to manoeuvre, the seemingly impossible can occur, with the ship ultimately succumbing to lateral motion, and touching the bottom, or hitting an obstruction on the port side.

Fig. 48 Working Astern in a Channel

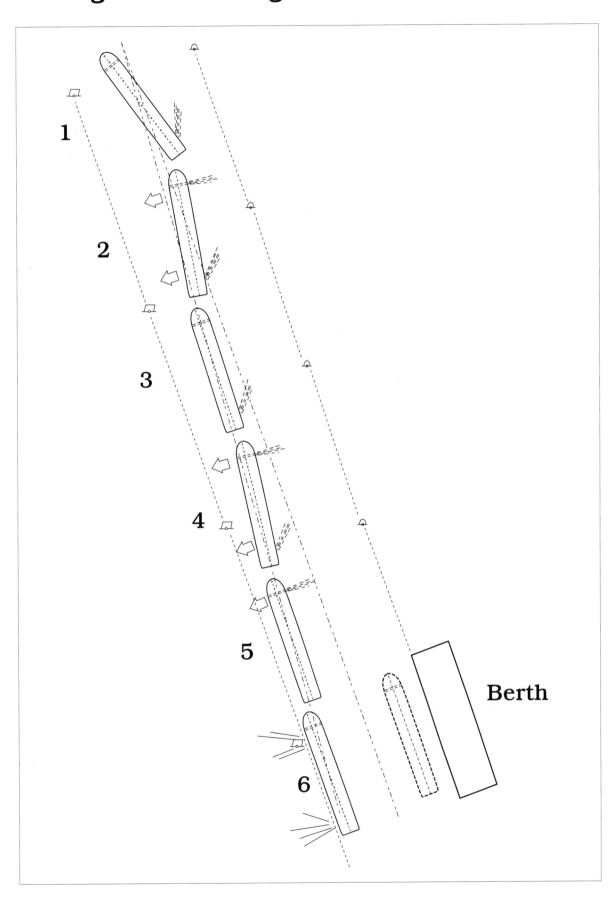

Fig. 49 Working Astern to a Berth

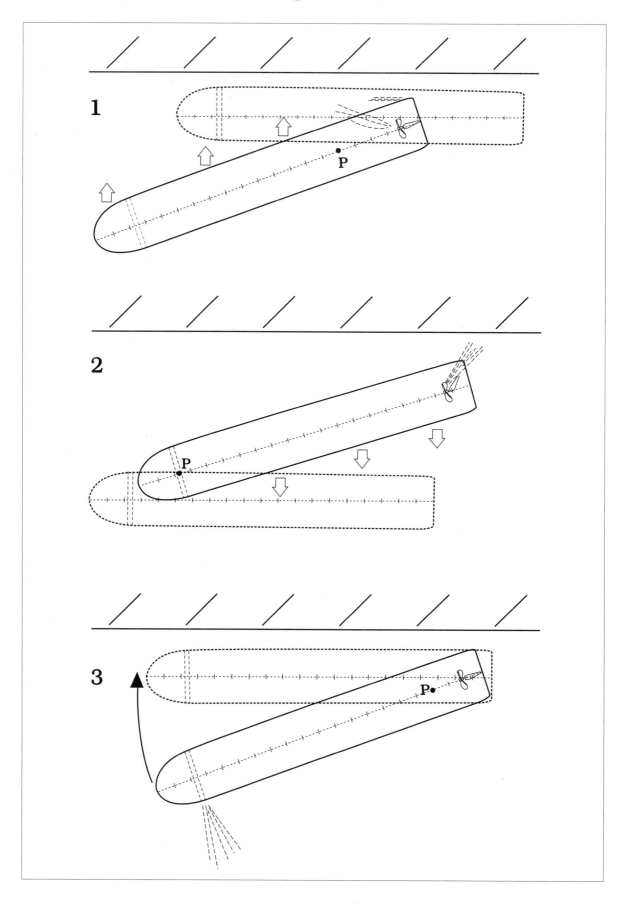

(It is not uncommon during this manoeuvre for large ships to engage one tug — which is secured aft — where it can assist very effectively with the steering and positioning of the stern, whilst the bow is controlled solely with the thruster.)

To avoid being caught in a similar manner, but keeping in mind that every movement is unique, with its own individual set of parameters, the following general tips may be of use ......

- get the ship moving smartly astern initially and then keep it moving. This avoids lingering under the effects of leeway or lateral motion, which are worse at slow speeds, or if the ship is allowed to stop.

- it is often tempting to use kicks ahead to reposition the stern. This can easily take all the way off the ship which may then, because it takes some time and effort to get a large vessel moving astern again, drift out of position with leeway. Use kicks ahead with caution!

- don't attempt it in winds that can easily override the thruster's meagre power.

- once the ship is moving astern, in order to limit transverse thrust to a minimum, take every opportunity to reduce or stop the stern power, until it is required to get the ship moving again.

- bring the stern round sufficiently to allow for transverse thrust when the stern power is brought in again.

- watch the heading carefully using the thruster boldly and vigorously to steer and keep the stern on the intended track, the rest will follow!

Working Astern to a berth
Fig. 49

Backing up to a berth on a ship with a bow thruster can be an especially rewarding and satisfying operation. It is particularly useful at resolving the difficulties that were discussed previously in this chapter, of working into a starboard side berth. This manoeuvre is shown in figure 49 and in the interests of clarity the important aspects of it are depicted with three separate illustrations.

Fig. 49
Position 1

When approaching the berth, it is important to remember where the pivot point is when the ship is making sternway because the orientation of the ship as it closes the dockside is fundamental to this manoeuvre. As the ship makes sternway it is, as a result of transverse thrust, apparently turning about its pivot point and tracking astern in a wide arc. This, in practical terms, means that the whole ship forward of the pivot point, some 125m in this case, is swinging to starboard as it slowly works astern.

By keeping the stern close up to the berth and heading for a point which leaves sufficient distance for the stern to work along the dockside, this tendency can then be used to swing all of the ship forward of the pivot point in towards the berth. If this natural bias of the ship is enhanced with the addition of a bow thruster, the positioning of the stern with the subsequent 'turning in' of the bow can be achieved with considerable confidence, making this a most satisfying manoeuvre.

Fig. 49
Position 2

One of the big advantages with approaching a berth stern first lies in the fact that the whole range of the ship's main power from dead slow ahead to full ahead is available as an enormous reserve of power, in this case 12,000 shp, with which it is relatively easy to correct the following ......

- an approach speed that is too high.
- inaccurate positioning of the stern.

If it is apparent as the ship approaches the berth that the speed of sternway is too high, or when it is time to stop the ship in any case, the main engine can be put ahead and this considerable power used to bring the ship to a fairly smart and abrupt halt. This excellent range of reserve power can also be used in the form of 'kicks ahead' to either bring the stern closer in to the dockside or alternatively lift it clear, thereby working the stern into the required position.

It is very important to be aware of the fact that if the ship is allowed to creep ahead, when using kicks ahead, at the instant it begins to make headway the pivot point moves to a position approximately $1/8$ of the length from forward. This means, in this example, with a kick ahead on full starboard rudder, that 175m of the ship aft of the pivot point will be swinging away from the dockside. Remember the difficulties discussed earlier, in developing lateral motion to starboard. This is extremely unwise and should be avoided at all costs, as it may be impossible to get the ship back, particularly with a light offshore wind!

Fig. 49
Position 3

If the stern is in position but the bow has not been brought in close enough, this need not be a problem, because if the ship is stopped and the bow thruster is used, the pivot point will move to a position right aft, and it will be working upon a good turning lever, thus producing its best turning moment with which to bring the bow alongside. This might cause the stern to drop away from the dockside slightly, but what movement there is can be checked with stern lines (or a single tug aft).

In situations when it is difficult to work the ship into a starboard side berth, perhaps because of an irritating offshore wind, it is often more expedient to use this method, and get the stern alongside and sorted out initially, before then using the thruster to work the bow in, as opposed to struggling with a seemingly instinctive and automatic determination to always get the bow in first.

Finally, it may be of interest to recall the discussion concerning the difficulties that can, unfortunately, develop when approaching a starboard side berth in the more customary manner, with headway and bow first. If the berth is proving totally unattainable, it is worth keeping in mind, provided there is sufficient water ahead of the ship, that it might be possible to run on a little past the berth, get the bow well round to port, and then work the ship back up to the berth stern first, in the same manner as illustrated in this chapter and figure 49.

Summary

It is the intention in this chapter to look at some of the advantages and disadvantages associated with bow thruster work. Those with little or no experience in working a single screw ship with the aid of a bow thruster will then have the prior knowledge in this area of ship handling and avoid some of those difficulties which are not always obvious before attempting a manoeuvre.

On smaller ships masters have to exercise their shiphandling skills in a wide variety of situations and frequently in critical circumstances

CHAPTER TEN

SPECIAL PROPELLERS AND RUDDERS

Introduction

THE MAJORITY OF VESSELS upon which most seafarers serve, have a traditional single, fixed pitch propeller and single rudder, which is designed primarily for getting the ship from one fairway buoy to another as economically as possible. This clearly leaves a lot to be desired in terms of manoeuvrability and this is not always acceptable, particularly in trades where the ship is frequently in the confines of pilotage waters.

In order to achieve a better compromise between manoeuvrability and economy some vessels may be fitted with propellers or rudders that differ considerably from the traditional, basic design. There are also a number vessels which are designed with a total commitment to manoeuvrability that have completely different propulsion and steering systems.

Unfortunately this type of ship is in a minority group. Many seafarers with a great deal of experience on conventional ships, and particularly trainee pilots, may occasionally find themselves boarding a ship that is fitted with a propulsion or steering system with which they are totally unfamiliar. With this in mind, this chapter will take a 'broad' look at some of the differing systems and the principles involved, with the hope that it will provide officers with a little general knowledge prior to boarding. This is the only objective of this chapter. It is not intended that it should be an in depth guide to 'specific' manufacturers' equipment.

Controllable Pitch Propellers

These propellers now have a relatively good track record for reliability and are becoming increasingly common on a wide range of tonnage. Unlike the fixed pitch propeller, the blades of these propellers can be altered, to set whatever pitch is required, across the whole power band from full ahead to full astern. This is usually achieved with hydraulic pumps or pistons, the older mechanical systems being less able to cope with the size and speeds of the modern vessel. The hydraulic pumps themselves are activated by an electric motor, which is in turn operated by remote bridge control. This may be either pneumatic or electronic. In small craft and in some older systems the bridge control may be mechanical, using cables linked direct to hydraulic rams, but these are becoming increasingly rare.

To use a controllable pitch (CP) propeller the main engine has to be clutched in, so that the propeller is continuously turning, usually at quite high revolutions. As it is neither practicable, nor economical, to run an engine continuously at excessively high rpm, it is important to have some sort of combined control over both rpm and pitch, so that the pitch for slow speeds is balanced with a reduction in revolutions. On most ships this is achieved by installing a 'combinator' which automatically balances engine revolutions against propeller pitch, thus producing a saving in fuel and better propeller performance.

Ahead Movements

To use ahead power, a ship with a CP propeller is not restricted to the stepped progression, through dead slow ahead to full ahead, that has for so long been associated with fixed pitch propellers. Any speed can be selected, simply by adjusting the combinator control to the required setting. It is also possible to set the propeller pitch for extremely low speeds, so that on those occasions when it is essential to proceed at very slow speeds, the propeller and rudder are still active and steerage way can be maintained for a lot longer than is usual. This is particularly advantageous if compared to the many ships with fixed pitch propellers, where the speed for dead slow ahead can sometimes be as high as five or six knots, due to excessive engine revolutions.

Slowing Down
Fig. 50(a)

When 'low speed' or 'stop' are demanded, the blades of the CP propeller are set with a very fine angle and pitch, to the extent that when they are viewed from astern, they will appear to open like a fan and the propeller will look rather like a closed disc or wheel. If the ship's speed is too high and does not already match the propeller speed, the flow of water through it will be restricted and a great deal of turbulence will develop behind the propeller, which will also have an adverse effect upon the rudder (see figure 50a).

If, therefore, the ship's speed is not reduced slowly and progressively, in much the same way as a large directionally unstable ship, the rudder will be shielded and the steering may become erratic or poor.

Whilst it is irritating if the steering is poor, it should not be forgotten that CP propellers are instantly available for corrective 'kicks ahead,' in a virtually unlimited supply, and are not liable to the restrictions that can be experienced with fixed pitch propellers, such as limited air supplies for starting the engine or delays whilst the engine is put ahead.

Transverse Thrust

One of the most common concerns mentioned by many officers, and quite rightly so, is the uncertainty as to which way the bow will cant, if at all, when a controllable pitch (CP) propeller is put astern. This is also something the pilot needs to know when he comes on board. To answer this question, it is necessary first to know which way the propeller is turning when it is viewed from astern. With the majority of CP propellers it is in an anticlockwise direction and they are called left-handed. It is important, however, when informed that a CP ship is left-handed, that it is not confused with a fixed pitch left-handed ship, because the CP propeller, it should be remembered, rotates the same way all the time. When the pitch is set for stern power, it is only the angle of the blades that has changed and the propeller is 'still' rotating anti clockwise or left-handed. The effect is now similar to a fixed pitch right-handed propeller working astern. The flow of water through the propeller is directed up onto the starboard quarter and may be strong enough to thrust the stern to port, so that the bow is seen to cant or 'kick' to starboard.

It is important to note that the transverse thrust on some ships with a CP propeller may be weak and unreliable,

Fig. 50 Controllable Pitch Propellers

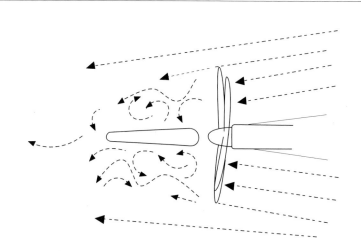

a) impeding the rudder with fine pitch settings

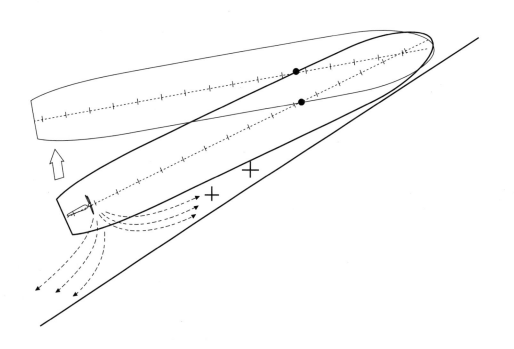

b) creating eddies and currents on zero pitch

due to vortices or turbulence around the propeller blades This is usually the result of specific design limitations and might, for example, occur when a CP propeller is designed to operate at slow speeds, with fine pitch settings, but high shaft revolutions. In another example, if the pitch is altered from ahead to astern, some of the inner or lower sections of the blades may be set at rather crude angles and this, too, can create vortices around the propeller. These characteristics can also have a detrimental effect on the maximum stern power available when compared to a similar ship with a fixed pitch propeller.

It is therefore advisable to exercise some caution when anticipating the effects of stern power on some CP ships.

Stopped and Alongside
Fig. 50(b)

On some ships, due to inferior design, age or poor maintenance, when the control stick on the bridge is positioned for stop with zero pitch, the propeller might not be accurately aligned to the same setting and some residual thrust may still exist. Although, with experience, a ship's master can compensate for this error, it is still imperative to remember that even though 'stop' has been requested, a ship with a CP propeller can unexpectedly creep ahead or astern.

This is very important during the period prior to slipping from a berth, when the engine is started and the shaft is clutched in. If the ropes are not kept tight, particularly while singling up, the vessel may start to move along the dockside, with serious consequences if other ships are tied up close ahead or astern. It is also noticeable on some ships that the CP propeller, which is constantly running with high revolutions, can pump quite a lot of water up onto the quarter and along the ship's side, even with zero pitch set. In the case of a left handed CP propeller this water will be flowing along the starboard side. If then, the ship is laying alongside a solid dockside, starboard side to and the ropes are slackened off, this can act like a tide flowing from astern and push the stern away from the dockside (see figure 50b). It can also make it very difficult to get the stern alongside when berthing, particularly when coming into a berth stern first and there has been a need to use stern power as well. This might not be resolved until either a stern line is ashore and tight, or the revolutions are reduced.

Breakdowns

It is inevitable that complex machinery, no matter how reliable, can eventually be exposed to the risk of failure. Whether this is a result of human error or negligence is another matter. What does matter is that it is not unknown, as a result of a breakdown in the system, particularly on some older ships, for a CP propeller to either stick, or abort to full ahead, stop, or full astern. On a modern vessel, in an effort to counteract this eventuality, the hydraulics, electric motors and bridge control are usually backed up with alternative systems, which can be activated by the ship's personnel in the event of a failure. This may of course take a little time. Whilst that might be acceptable in open waters, it would not be satisfactory within the confines of pilotage waters where, for example, a short period of time with a propeller stuck at full power could result in a serious accident!

It is therefore worth bearing in mind, that there should be an 'emergency stop' button on the bridge with which to either stop the engine, or declutch the propeller, in an emergency. Finally, if power to the propeller is lost, it is helpful if the propeller's pitch can be set to full ahead, so that the rudder is not shielded and can be used to some effect with what steerage way remains.

Propeller Shrouds
Fig. 51(a) and (b)

In Europe, some years ago, trials were conducted with a vessel whose propeller was placed inside a tube-like shroud or tunnel. The hope was that it would restrict a propeller's wash to a smaller arc and so reduce the erosion of canal and river banks by passing traffic. Whilst this was, indeed, successful, more significantly it was noticed that a vessel fitted with a shrouded propeller was considerably more powerful than a comparable vessel with an unshrouded propeller. Today many vessels, ranging from tugs to the wide variety of traffic using inland waterways, including some coasters, may be fitted with shrouded propellers. Although not common on larger deep sea ships, some do exist and one or two shipyards have even built the occasional VLCC with the propeller encased in a shroud of truly gigantic proportions!

The increase in power output from the propeller, which can be either fixed or controllable pitch, is achieved by making the diameter within the shroud smaller than the forward end (see figure 51a). Because of this, the propeller is constantly drawing a mass of water into the shroud which then has to be forced out through a smaller aperture. For this to happen, the water has to be ejected out of the shroud at a much higher velocity than it entered and, as a result, a positive pressure exists at the aft end of the shroud. It is this which gives the vessel its additional lift or drive, rather like a circular aerofoil! The shroud also improves performance by removing some of the losses associated with the flow of water at the tips of the propeller blades, thereby making them more effective.

If a shroud is installed on a large single screw ship, it is usually rigidly attached to the ship's stern rather like a fixed tunnel. In other cases however the shroud, together with its propeller, may rotate as one unit and effectively become a nozzle or azimuth drive. These can be installed as single or twin units and although some coasters may be found with azimuth stern drives, the most common example is the azimuth drive tug, which usually has twin units, either amidships or aft (see figure 51b). The design of tugs has benefited enormously from shroud technology, as it enables bollard pull to be increased economically, without installing larger engines and incurring the penalties of higher capital expenditure and rising fuel bills.

It is especially effective at low speeds and high loads. At zero forward speed and full power (the bollard pull condition) about 50% of the thrust comes from the duct alone. At high speeds the drag of the duct is detrimental to its efficiency.

Whilst the fitting of a shroud to the propeller of a conventional single screw ship is primarily a matter of economic consideration and not one of manoeuvrability, it

Fig. 51 Propeller Shrouds

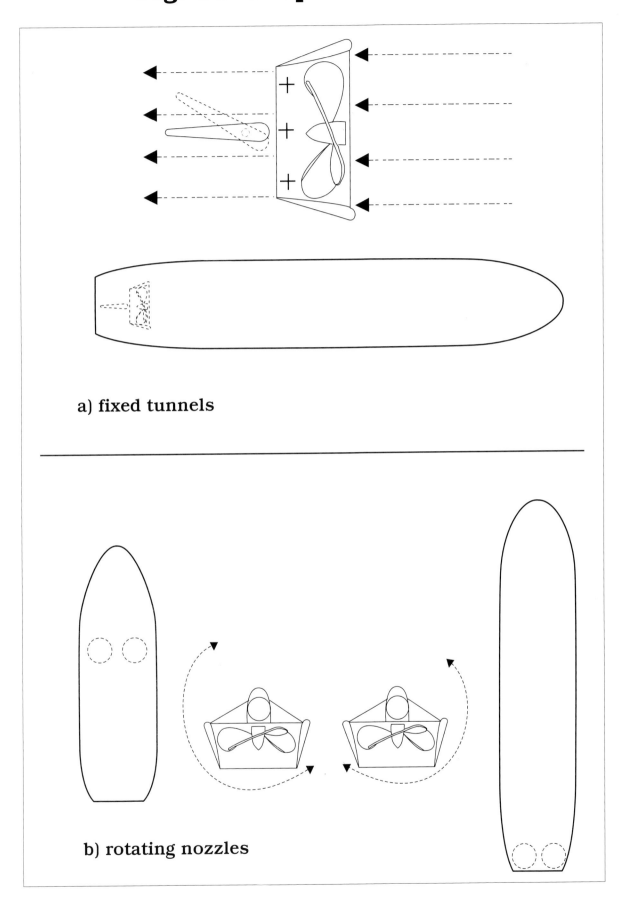

a) fixed tunnels

b) rotating nozzles

must, nevertheless, be of some consequence with regards to its handling characteristics. It is quite possible, for example, that the higher velocity of water flow from the shroud onto the rudder will improve both the quality of steering and the response to kicks ahead at low speeds. The shroud, rather like a skeg, may also give better directional stability to the ship. These points are, however, difficult to quantify and may not be particularly noticeable when onboard a ship. What is more noticeable is the effect of a shroud when the propeller is put astern.

Transverse thrust

In normal circumstances, when a conventional right-handed propeller is going astern, the water flows diagonally through it and part of that water flow is then deflected up onto the ship's starboard side. If on the other hand it is placed in a shroud, the usual water flow into and out of the propeller is restricted, to the extent that very little is directed up onto the starboard quarter.

Assuming it is not influenced by any other external forces, this means that it is possible for a ship with a shrouded propeller to run in a relatively straight line when slowing down or stopping because there will be no cant of the bow when the propeller is put astern. On the negative side, however, it must be remembered that the fixed shroud is designed for efficiency when making headway and not sternway, so when compared to a similar ship with an unshrouded propeller, the stern power is very poor.

Blockages

It is not unknown, particularly on tugs or coastal ships with azimuth drives and constantly running, controllable pitch propellers, for foreign objects to be sucked into the shroud and jam with such force that the engine either stops, or has to be stopped, because the excess load is causing the engine temperatures to rise unacceptably. This usually occurs in shallow, fast flowing, tidal rivers and estuaries, when foreign objects, such as lorry tyres and goodness knows what else have been thrown into the upper reaches of the river and work their way down stream. There are no immediate answers to this problem, other than to keep a sharp lookout for any rubbish in the water and be aware that it can happen! In the long term it can only be hoped that pollution controls will improve.

Rudders
Conventional Rudders
Fig. 52(a) and (b)

The traditional or conventional rudder, employed world wide in thousands of ships, is unfortunately, from a ship handling point of view, something of a compromise between economy and necessity. On sea passages it is continuously being worked, with a succession of small rudder angles, for normal steering purposes and at modest speeds large alterations of course are easily achieved within the customary 35° of maximum rudder angle. For this fairly simple requirement the rudder, together with its associated hydraulic pumps and electric motors, does not need to be unduly large or complex and will therefore be relatively economical in terms of both installation and running costs.

Whilst bigger more expensive units could be installed, this would not be advantageous, because the basic rudder is not hydrodynamically efficient beyond an angle of 35°, or in some cases 45°. At any stage up to this angle and 'hard over,' the rudder retains a smooth water flow across

Fig. 52 Conventional Rudders

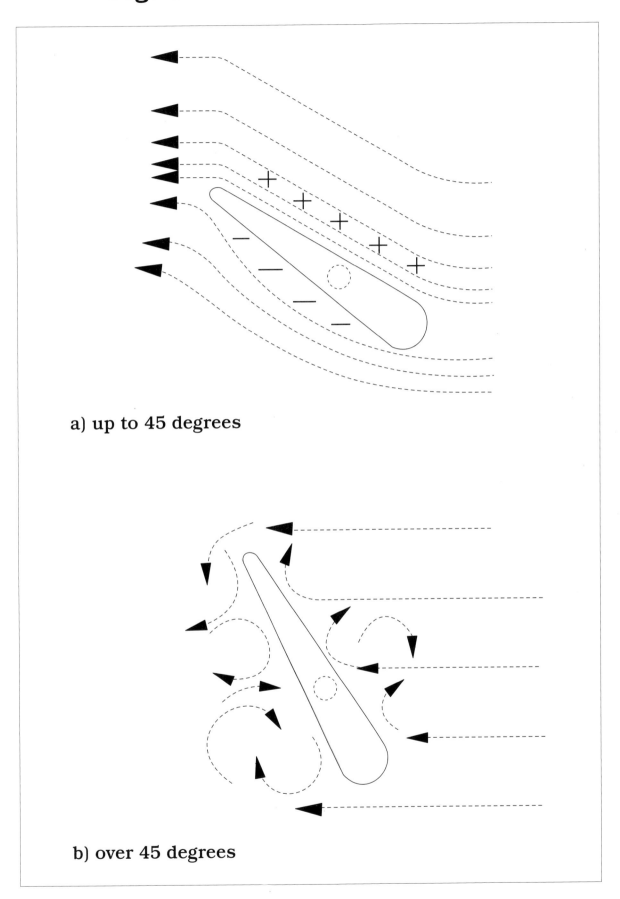

a) up to 45 degrees

b) over 45 degrees

Fig. 53 Alternative Rudder Designs

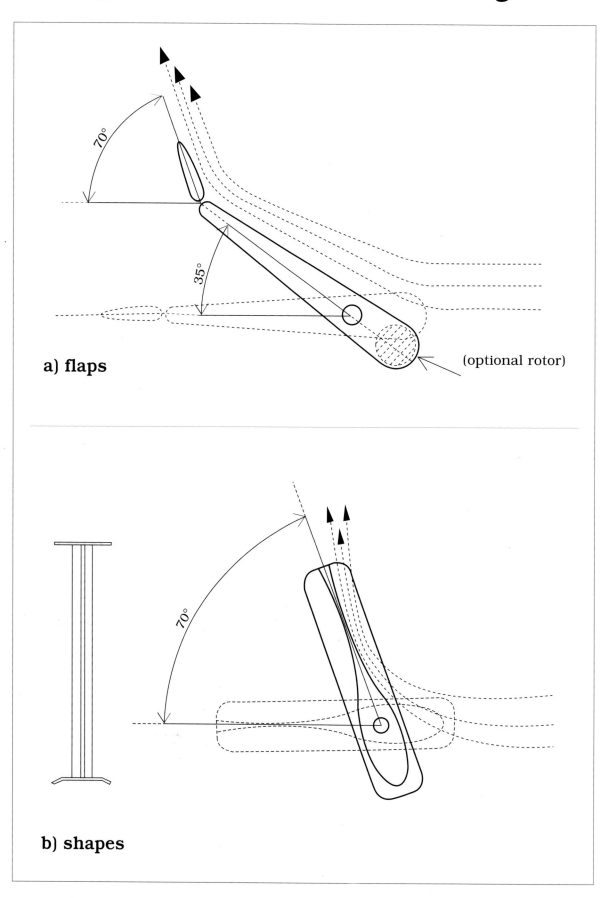

70°

35°

a) flaps

(optional rotor)

70°

b) shapes

both faces and this creates a positive pressure on one side, but equally important, a negative pressure on the opposite side and this gives the rudder, rather like an aircraft's wing, its lift (see figure 52a).

Unfortunately, at any angle exceeding 45°, the water flow across the rudder, particularly on the low pressure side, becomes progressively more turbulent, until eventually the rudder stalls and it is rendered much less effective (see figure 52b). As a result of this limitation, the conventional rudder, although satisfactory on passage, is somewhat restricted when it comes to manoeuvrability at slow speeds in confined waters. The exception, perhaps, is the 45° rudder, which in comparison to the more common 35° rudder does perform a little better with regard to turning ability. It is, nevertheless, still a conventional rudder and manufacturers have had to look at alternative designs to improve rudder performance.

Rudder Flaps and Rotors Fig. 53(a)

There are quite a few ships in service which are now fitted with what is essentially a conventional rudder, but with an additional 'flap' on the trailing or aftermost edge of the rudder. These are not unlike the flaps that are deployed on the wings of aircraft and which generate extra lift during take off and landing. When the helm is put over, the main rudder can be set at any angle up to a maximum of 35,° in the normal manner, and as the main rudder rotates the flap automatically articulates with it until a maximum angle of 70° is reached (see figure 53a). The progressive nature of this articulation, in terms of rudder angles, ensures a smooth flow of water over the rudder and flap at all times with good lift and a much improved turning ability over conventional rudders. In some cases, water flow around the rudder may also be enhanced by a rotating cylinder, mounted vertically, on the leading edge of the main rudder. Individual designs vary according to specific manufacturers so that some rudders may have flaps, others rotors and some rotors and flaps. They all however, give excellent performance. These types of rudder are most commonly known as either **'Becker'** or **'Jastram'** rudders.

Shaped Rudders Fig. 53(b)

This is an alternative design to the flap and one where the manufacturer has shaped the rudder so that it can be turned to angles of up to 70° and yet still retain excellent performance (see figure 53b). The forebody of the rudder is elliptical in shape, but runs into a rear body section which is concave. The top and bottom of the rudder is constructed with flanges, which help to channel or contain the water flow across the rudder face as it runs into the concave section, before being deflected out at a sharp angle at the aft end of the rudder. This type of rudder is commonly known as the **'Single Schilling Rudder'**.

Operational Aspects

Although all of these specialised rudders deploy to 70° they are still used in much the same way as conventional rudders, but with the advantage of excellent turning ability from the correct use of kicks ahead. When worked in conjunction with a good bow thruster it is possible to develop outstanding lateral motion and care needs to be exercised when landing on the dockside or upon other ships, in case the ship's sideways movement is excessive.

With many of these rudders able to rotate to angles of 70° or more on ships which are capable of moderately high speeds, it is not surprising that enormous loads can be placed upon the rudder and its associated systems. Although the rudder and steering gear are built to withstand these loads, without some safeguards they could be seriously damaged. For this reason, some ships with specialised rudders may be fitted with a system override which will limit the use or the angle of the rudders to 35° when the ship's speed exceeds a certain speed. This might, for example, be at around 5 or 6 knots.

Twin Schilling Rudders
Fig. 54

This innovative system may now be found on an increasing number of vessels. Although in the past these were mainly of smaller tonnage, the system may now be found on a range of new larger vessels which pilots around the world may find themselves boarding on occasions. Unlike the single flap or shaped rudders that were illustrated in figure 53 and which are used in much the same manner as conventional rudders, this system is totally different in both design and operation.

The most unusual but essential feature of this system is the propeller, which even though it is fixed pitch, is constantly running with the main engine permanently on ahead revolutions. For ship handling purposes, the optimum rpm required are those which are normally associated with manoeuvring full ahead, although this can be adjusted, if so required, for example to reduce excessive wash.

Immediately astern of the propeller, in place of the conventional rudder, are two Schilling rudders each of which can rotate through a total arc of 145° (see figure 54). They are set up so that each rudder has an arc of operation either side of the fore and aft line ranging from an inner angle of 35° right round to an outer angle of 110°. The rudders do not act independently of each other but are instead synchronised to work in harmony with each other in response to a single joystick control on the bridge which is extremely easy to operate.

In figure 54 four important rudder positions are illustrated, each of which is in response to a specific joystick setting. The joystick can be adjusted as required to obtain a wide range of intermediate rudder positions.

Full Ahead
Fig. 54(a)

This is the position for normal full ahead with the joystick fully forward. If the joystick is eased back the rudders progressively open outwards, deflecting the propeller's wash or drive and thus reducing the ship's speed.

Bow to Port
Fig. 54(b)

If the joystick is put forward and to port at the maximum setting, one rudder goes to 35° and the other to 70°. This gives excellent turning ability, particularly at slow speeds.

Full Astern
Fig. 54(c)

To obtain stern power up to the equivalent of full astern, the joystick is pulled right back until each rudder has rotated right around to 110° thus closing the gap between them. The propeller's wash is then deflected

Fig. 54 Twin Schilling Rudders

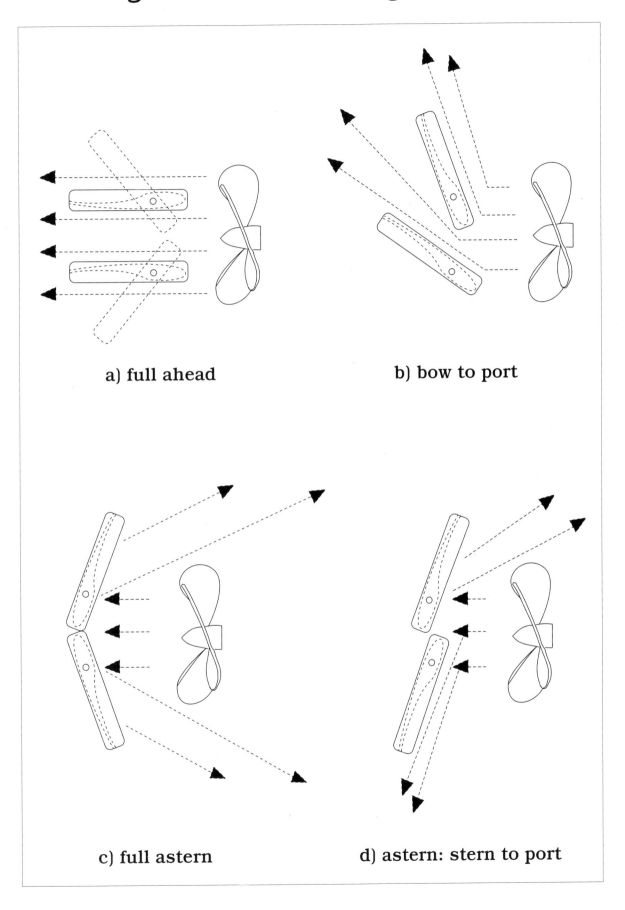

a) full ahead

b) bow to port

c) full astern

d) astern: stern to port

forwards and works in much the same way as the reverse thrust of an aircraft's jet engine, when it is deployed to stop the aircraft after touch down.

The equivalent of the conventional 'stop engine' is obtained by adjusting the joystick to the appropriate intermediate neutral setting, so that the rudders are rotated to a position somewhere between full ahead (figure 54a) and full astern (figure 54c), which gives neither forward nor astern thrust. This varies a little, because the propeller wash is then deflected sideways and may be effected by such things as depth under the keel, tides, or the close proximity of solid jetties.

Astern: Stern to port Figure 54(d)

This figure illustrates one of the most beneficial characteristics of these rudders and one which gives good control of the ship's head, when either slowing down, stopping, or backing, with the rudders deployed for astern thrust. In this particular example the joystick has been eased across in the direction of the port quarter and this will rotate and open out the appropriate rudder so that the stern is also thrust to port. This is extremely useful, bearing in mind that it is not always so easy to keep control of the ship's head and speed at the same time, when as an alternative the rudders are employed for kicks ahead.

Whilst this system, with its constantly running propeller, seems a little strange at first, most officers, after a short period of instruction, appear to get the feel of it relatively quickly.

Summary

This chapter has only been concerned with conventional cargo carrying ships, which might have a propulsion or steering system that is little different from the traditional single rudder and fixed pitch propeller. The objective herein is to furnish inexperienced personnel with a broad knowledge of some of the more common systems. There are other more complex systems in service, on dynamic positioning (DP) vessels for example, but these are highly sophisticated and will always require highly trained and specialised operators.

CHAPTER ELEVEN

TWIN SCREW WORK

Introduction

WHILST IT MAY SEEM a little strange at first, the techniques for working a twin screw ship are usually picked up quite quickly. Unless the ship is especially cumbersome or unwieldy it doesn't take long to get the feel of the ship. This is particularly so for masters and officers permanently employed on twin screw ships, such as short haul ferries and cruise ships, where they are able to gain considerable experience driving a twin screw ship. It soon becomes second nature. There are, however, one or two important points that may be worth looking at and which might be of use to those less fortunate personnel who have little or no experience of twin screw work but may occasionally find themselves boarding such a ship.

The essence of twin screw work and a good twin screw ship, is not the result of any one factor alone, but rather several important factors which can combine to produce excellent handling characteristics. These are ......

- **the rudder configuration**.
- **the effect of torque**.
- **the effect of transverse thrust**.
- **the pivot point**.
- **turning ability**.

The rudder configuration
Fig. 55

Initially this might seem a somewhat odd topic to discuss, as it is all too easy to assume that the rudders are adequately designed for the task. There are, however, a few ships in service, in particular some older generation container ships, which although twin screw are unfortunately built with only one rudder. On this type of ship the rudder is situated on the centre line between the two propellers. Even when 'hard over' it may be either wholly or partially out of the propellers helical discharge (see figure 55a). This means that response to the rudder is exceptionally poor at very slow speeds, because it may be solely reliant upon ship's speed, and not propeller wash to generate water flow across it.

This is most noticeable when getting under way from stopped. The ship takes a long time to answer the helm and travels quite some distance in the interim time interval. If this type of ship is exposed to any adverse manoeuvring conditions, such as shallow water or contrary winds and tides, it is likely to become seriously unmanageable at slow speeds and considerable care should be exercised, with some emphasis upon the need for adequate tug support.

In view of experiences such as this, it is desirable to have two rudders on twin propeller ships, so that each rudder is positioned within the helical discharge of an individual propeller. They can then work interactively, in the same manner as the propeller and rudder on a single screw ship.

The effect of torque

The term torque is used in this instance to describe the natural turning effect that is created by one engine

Fig. 55 Twin Screw Configurations

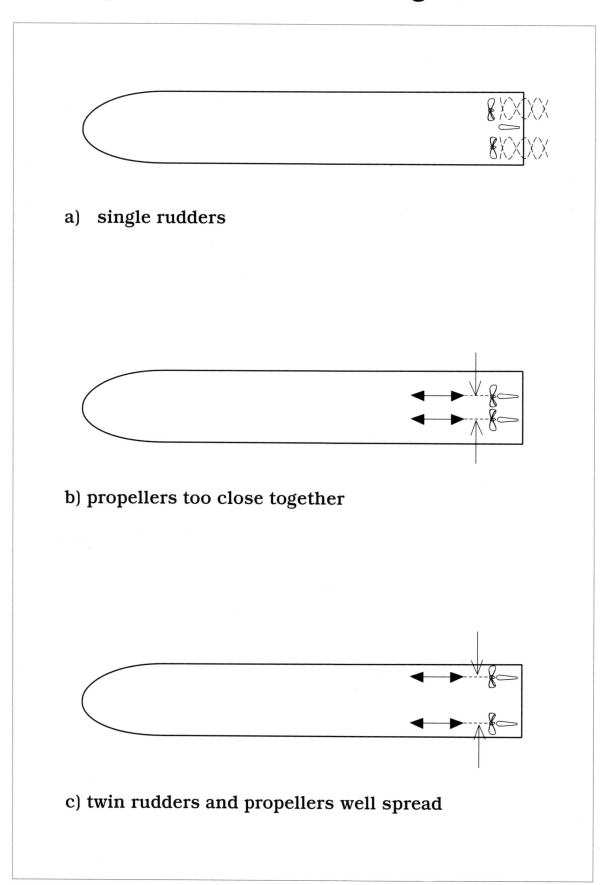

a)   single rudders

b) propellers too close together

c) twin rudders and propellers well spread

Fig. 55(b)

pushing ahead and one engine pulling astern or, to a lesser extent, just one of those engines being used. This contributes towards good twin screw turning ability, but occasionally it is possible to come across a ship where the effect will be extremely disappointing, because the ship is designed with the propellers too close together (see figure 55b).

A few specialised ships, such as sail training ships with auxiliary power and some low powered naval vessels, are naturally narrow beamed and especially poor. In the worst cases a prolonged period with one engine ahead and the other astern, even with full power, will produce an insignificant or negligible rate of turn. In these circumstances the master will often advise, quite correctly, that the propellers are used together as one, in much the same manner as a single screw ship.

Fig. 55(c)

In view of the problems associated with handling twin screw ships with single rudders, or propellers too close together, or both, a better design is one where there are twin rudders and where the propellers have as much athwartships spacing as possible (see figure 55c). Having said this, it is possible to go from one extreme to the other and board a ship where the propeller blades extend well out beyond the fore and aft line of the ships side. With this type of ship, when close to the dockside during berthing and unberthing, the master may have no choice but to insist that the inboard propeller is stopped and in the case of controllable pitch propellers, the shafts as well.

Fortunately, if they are on a regular run, ships with these unique handling problems tend to become well known within a pilotage district and individual pilots are forewarned before boarding them. There will always, however, be exceptions and many pilots around the world may not have previous experience of this type of ship.

The effect of transverse thrust

It is essential that when the appropriate propeller is put astern to assist turning ability that the transverse thrust is directed up onto the correct quarter. To ascertain if this is so it is necessary to look at the direction of rotation of each propeller, when viewed from astern, and determine whether they are either ......

- **'outward' turning**,
  or
- **'inward' turning**.

Outward Turning Fixed Pitch Propellers Fig. 56(a) and (b)

In relationship to each other when going ahead, the blades of these propellers are outward turning in the upper half of their circle of rotation, when viewed from astern (see figure 56a). If however, the starboard propeller is put astern, to assist for example in turning the ship to starboard, it will now be rotating in the opposite direction (see figure 56b). This propeller is therefore behaving in exactly this same way as the right-handed propeller on a single screw ship and part of its helical discharge will be deflected up and onto the starboard quarter. The resultant transverse thrust will cant the bow to starboard, not only assisting the turn, but also working in conjunction with both the rudders and propeller torque.

Fig. 56 Twin Fixed Pitch Propellers —
Outward Turning

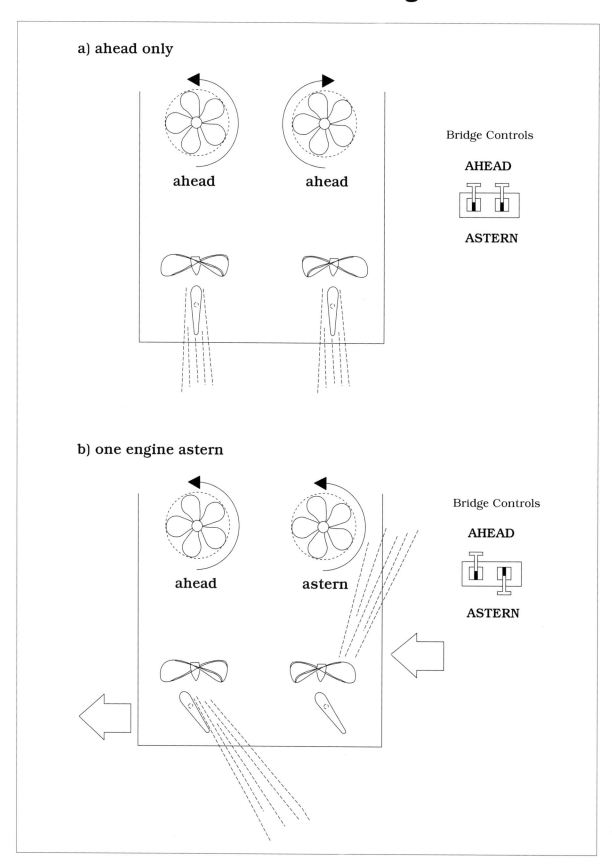

a) ahead only

ahead   ahead

Bridge Controls

AHEAD

ASTERN

b) one engine astern

ahead   astern

Bridge Controls

AHEAD

ASTERN

Fig. 57 Twin Fixed Pitch Propellers — Inward Turning

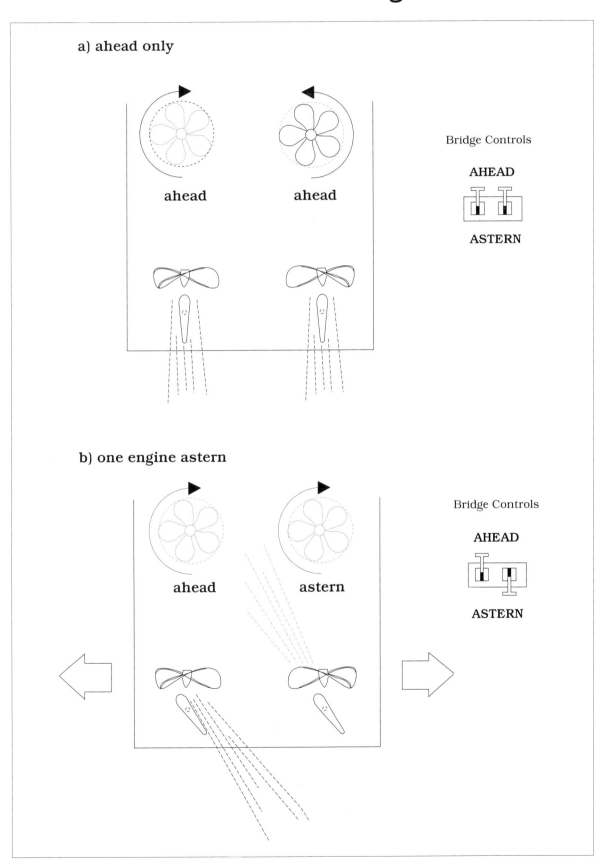

a) ahead only

ahead   ahead

Bridge Controls

AHEAD

ASTERN

b) one engine astern

ahead   astern

Bridge Controls

AHEAD

ASTERN

Inward Turning Fixed
Pitch Propellers
Fig. 57(a) and (b)

These propellers, when viewed from astern, are now inward turning in the upper half of their circle of rotation (see figure 57a). If, once again, the ship is turning to starboard and the starboard propeller is put astern to assist, it will be rotating in the opposite direction (see figure 57b). This propeller is acting in the same way as a left-handed propeller on a single screw ship so, whilst going astern, part of the helical discharge will be deflected up and towards the port quarter! The resultant transverse thrust will attempt to cant the bow to port, not only in the opposite direction to the desired turn, but also working against the rudders and propeller torque. The astern wash from the starboard propeller may also seriously deflect the smooth flow of water from the port propeller onto its own rudder.

The effect of inward turning propellers upon a ship can be extremely severe and render it totally unmanageable from a ship handling point of view. In the worst case it has been found necessary, when manoeuvring, to stop one engine completely and work the vessel in the same manner as a single screw ship. It is difficult to imagine why ships are built with inward turning propellers if they are so difficult to handle, but apparently this configuration does give a better economical performance in terms of fuel consumption, particularly on long passages!

Controllable Pitch
Propellers

With a CP propeller rotating the same way all the time it can, at first, seem a little confusing when trying to understand whether they should be inward or outward turning for twin screw work. To work this out it is best to start with the assumption that the inside propeller during a turn must, when it is set with astern pitch, give transverse thrust onto the appropriate quarter. Looking at figure 56b the starboard propeller would therefore need to be turning anticlockwise or left-handed, but looking at figure 57b the port propeller would need to rotating clockwise or right-handed. The two CP propellers thus need to be inward turning or 'handed' as it is sometimes called, in order to achieve the same results as outward turning fixed pitch propellers.

Although, in general, ships are built to give the correct twin screw response, there are in fact a few ships in existence which do not have handed twin CP propellers, but instead have twin propellers which rotate the same way and they may be either right or left-handed. It can actually be difficult to ascertain from the ship's personnel which way they turn until stern power is used and it is possible to see which way the bow cants. This is another example of an unusual case where again, it is best to use the two propellers as one, rather like a single screw ship.

The Pivot Point

Irrespective of what rudder and propeller configuration a ship has, the fundamental principles concerning the pivot point and the forces involved remain the same. All of those principles which were relevant to the handling of a single screw ship are of equal importance when working a twin screw ship, the only difference being the greater variety of options available in terms of engine power.

It should still be borne in mind, when the ship is backing, that the pivot point will be approximately a $1/4$ of the ships length from the stern and that any forces created by the propellers, whether astern or ahead, will be working upon a small turning lever and therefore generating relatively poor turning moments (see figure 58a). The only exception to this would be extremely powerful vessels, such as a modern warship, where the immense power can have a tendency to conceal this fact.

On the other hand, when the ship is making headway, the pivot point will move to a position roughly $1/8$ to $1/3$ of the ships length from forward and vary according to the ship's speed and whether it is turning or steady. If the propellers are now used either ahead or astern they will be working upon a much better turning lever and produce excellent turning moments (see figure 58b). In view of this some masters, when turning a twin screw ship in a restricted area, prefer to back up as far as practicable first, and then make some headway whilst turning, because it results in a much better rate of turn. Again the only exception would be immensely powerful ships, where the difference is not discerned and there is a tendency to turn on the spot.

Turning Ability

The ability to develop rate of turn, with a twin screw ship of modest power, is perhaps best viewed in two different categories ......

- **low speed manoeuvring**.
- **manoeuvring at higher speeds**.

Turning ability at low speed

Like any other ship manoeuvring at low speeds, often within the confines of a port complex, the turning ability of a twin screw ship has constantly to be balanced with the need to monitor the ship's speed and keep it under control. The big advantage of a twin screw ship, and this is perhaps the best way to view it, is that the appropriate engine can be used ahead with full rudder to develop what is essentially a prolonged 'kick ahead' whilst the other engine is used astern, to keep the speed down.

By going astern on the inside engine the ship is kept permanently in the first stage of a standing turn, with the pivot point approximately $1/8$L from the bow and lateral resistance to the turn constantly low (see chapter 4 — Turning — figure 7). The engine which is going ahead and its associated rudder are therefore permanently working on an excellent turning lever with minimal lateral resistance. The engines can of course be balanced as so required to either maintain headway, stop, or ease the ship back, but it should be remembered that this will shift the pivot point and affect turning ability accordingly.

At that point during ship handling, when ahead power can no longer be used and stern power has to be used to stop the vessel, the twin screw ship is something of a luxury over the single screw ship. Any undesirable cant of the bow with stern power can be checked by adjusting the balance of power between the two engines as they are going astern and, if so required, this can also be used to develop small rates of turn which gives fine control over the bow while stopping.

Fig. 58 Twin Screw Turning Ability

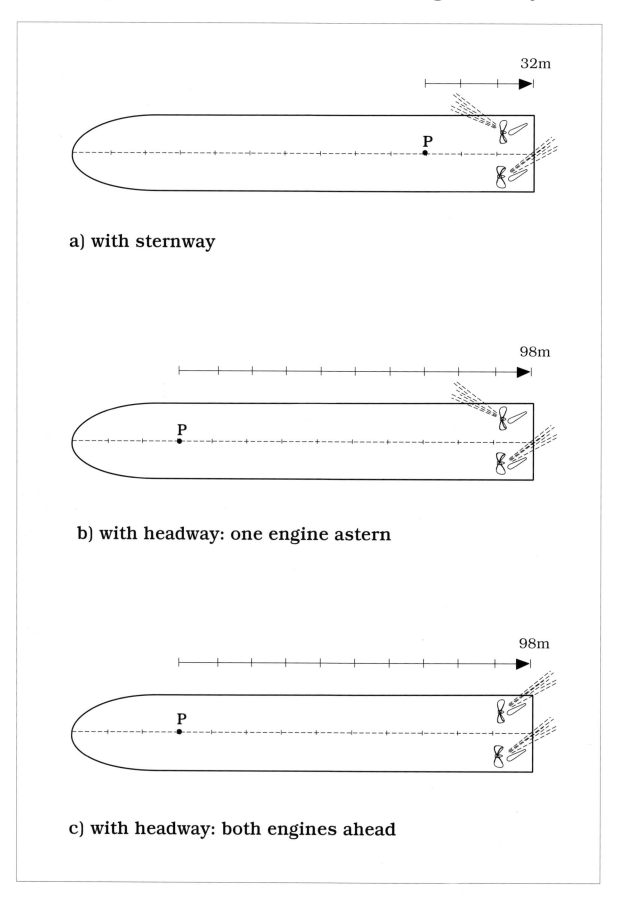

a) with sternway

b) with headway: one engine astern

c) with headway: both engines ahead

Turning ability at speed
Fig. 58(c)

When handling a twin screw ship at moderate speeds however, often in the confines of a channel, river or estuary, it is worth recalling some of the points which were relevant to handling single screw ships ......

- transverse thrust is a poor turning force.

- the wash from a propeller going astern and therefore transverse thrust, will not reach the hull if the speed is too high.

- the rudder force generated with ahead power is an excellent turning force.

- constant speed turning circles are always similar no matter what the speed.

- correctly applied 'kicks ahead' are the most effective way to tighten a turn.

These points are particularly significant because there is often an automatic tendency with inexperience, to rely upon backing one engine to tighten a difficult turn, at a bend in a channel for instance. Whilst this is absolutely fine at low manoeuvring speeds it is very unwise at a moderate speeds, for example over 5 or 6 knots. This is because transverse thrust is a poor force, in comparison to rudder force and it will actually result in a reduction of the vessels rate of turn and a larger turning circle.

Alternatively, the rudders could be put hard over and both engines used with sufficient power to generate kicks ahead which will, if the speed is not excessive, result in a much tighter turning circle (see figure 58c). This will be extremely important, when negotiating a difficult turn with adverse conditions, such as shallow water or high adverse winds.

As so often is the case, excessive speed is the greatest enemy and it must always be brought well down, before the advantages of either kicks ahead or twin screw work can be fully utilised.

Conventional tugs are still used in many ports of the world

An Azimuth Stern Drive tug demonstrating its versatility

CHAPTER TWELVE

TUGS IN SHIP HANDLING

Introduction

THERE ARE, THROUGHOUT THE HARBOURS, offshore installations and waterways of the world, a diverse range of maritime operations, each of which has its own working practices concerning the use of tugs. These will have developed as a result of specific operational demands within an individual pilot's district which may have been influenced by some or all of the following ......

- **type of ships being served.**
- **number of ships being turned around.**
- **environmental conditions.**
- **navigational constraints.**
- **size and type of tugs available.**
- **fiscal considerations.**
- **inherent historic or traditional practices.**
- **experience levels of personnel involved.**

Given such a wide sphere of operations across the world, it is obviously difficult to develop general instructional material for tug operations. Not surprisingly, in some cases, it may come into conflict with more specific individual working methods which naturally take priority and this is fully appreciated and understood.

A pilot's initial expertise with the use of tugs is frequently restricted to what can be gleaned from the advice of senior pilots and colleagues during training, sometimes a brief period as an observer on a tug, and thereafter personal experience.

With these points in mind this chapter is intended solely as a basis from which to start and to assist officers and pilots in developing or reinforcing their own ideas and experience when using tugs.

To gain a broad insight into the use of tugs, it is first important to be aware of the types of tug commonly available and in particular their strengths or weaknesses. To do this it is helpful, to group the many different types of tugs according to their working methods and this provides the following broad categories ......

- **conventional tugs.**
- **tractor tugs.**
- **azimuth stern drive tugs (ASD).**

Conventional Tugs
Fig. 59(a) and (b)

The conventional or traditional tug, for years the work horse of the maritime industry and still widely employed, has two inherent design features which can, by modern standards, limit its efficiency. These are ......

- **the traditional propulsion unit.**
- **the position of the towing hook.**

The propulsion unit is usually a single right or left handed propeller with a standard rudder configuration, not unlike many small vessels world wide. To increase

Fig. 59 Conventional Tug

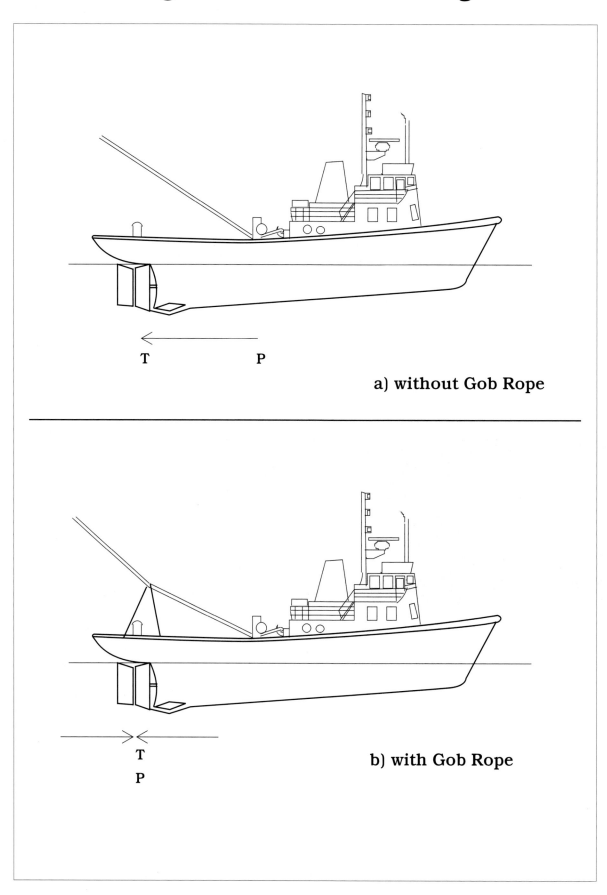

a) without Gob Rope

b) with Gob Rope

bollard pull, with the installed power unit, the propeller may be placed in a shroud or rotating nozzle, some may have controllable pitch screws and some may be twin screwed. Whilst they may be economical, powerful, have good sea keeping qualities and be well proven over the years, they may, nevertheless, by modern standards, be restricted by fairly basic manoeuvrability.

This means that the conventional tug, if required to do so by the pilot, might be slow and sometimes limited in its ability to reposition quickly. The tug's master must also be very careful to avoid difficult situations whereby the tug may become trapped and unable to manoeuvre freely to a safer position, if it is beyond its handling capabilities.

Like most traditional vessels, propulsion is at the stern, and this dictates the design position of the towing hook. When a tug is making way as an ordinary vessel, with no tow connected, or when making way and towing, but the tow line is slack, the pivot point will be approximately a $1/4$ of the length of the tug from forward and the tug may be expected to handle like any other conventional vessel.

Once however, a tow is connected (see figure 59a) and the tug takes the weight, it is likely that the pivot point (P) will move aft towards the position of the towing point or hook, which will usually be as far forward as design permits and as near amidships as possible. Although the distance of (**P**) from the propeller and therefore thrust (**T**) is now reduced, it is still substantial and the tug retains a good turning moment (**PT**) and a fair degree of manoeuvrability under the tow .

If , however, any attempt is made to rigidly fix the tow, at or closer to the stern (see figure 59b) it results in a large or total reduction of (PT), which will affect a serious loss of manoeuvrability. The towing hook therefore needs to be positioned as far forward of the propulsion unit as possible, thus allowing the tug freedom of movement under the tow line.

This combination of towing hook amidships and limited manoeuvrability, have a tendency to place the conventional tug at particular risk to either interaction or girting.

Interaction Forward

In 1950 a leading tug manufacturer conducted a research programme into a large number of tug accidents, all of which had resulted in the loss of life. The most common cause of these accidents was found to be 'interaction'. Since then the size of ships using tugs has increased enormously and the tug, still relatively small and often working alongside, must be very much more at risk from this invisible phenomenon.

In simple terms, a ship making headway through the water has zones of differing water pressures surrounding it. This results in a positive pressure forward of its pivot point extending out from the ship, whilst a low pressure or suction area exists all the way down the ship's side from the pivot point to the propeller (see chapter 7 — Interaction). Near the stern this suction area is augmented

Fig. 60 Tug Interaction

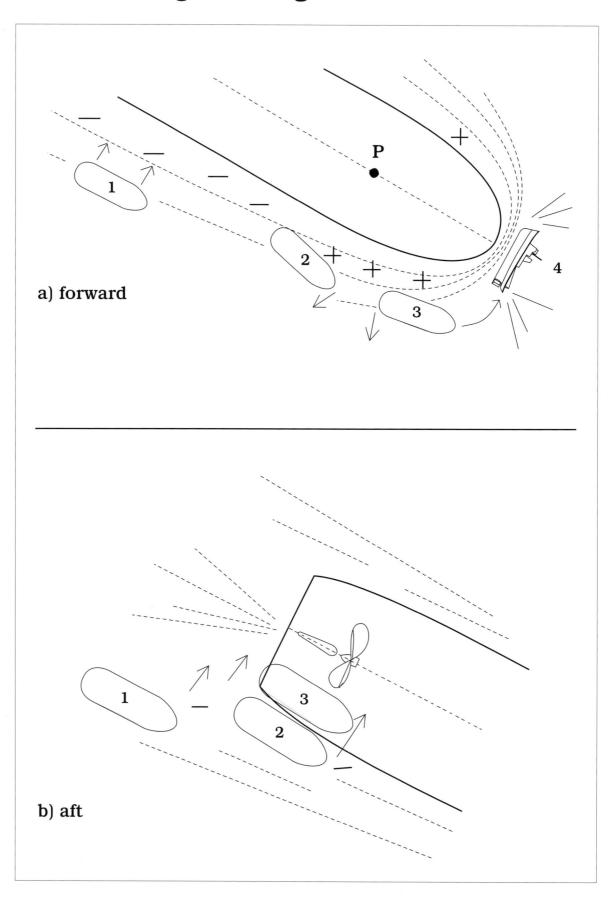

a) forward

b) aft

by the flow of water into the propeller aperture whilst the engine is turning ahead and, it should be noted, at any time whilst controllable pitch propellers are engaged.

Fig. 60(a)

It should be remembered that the strength of these interaction zones and the distance they extend out from the ship can increase dramatically, not only with a small increase in ship speed but also if the ship passes into shallow water and the pressure zones are restricted. When a tug is working its way in towards the ship's forebody, with the intention of passing a line forward, it may pass through one or more of these important areas (see figure 60a) and experience adverse handling characteristics.

Fig. 60(a)
Position 1

In position 1 for example and similarly all the way down the side of the ship, if the tug is allowed to get in too close, it might, despite all the efforts to prevent it, be bodily and inexplicably sucked into the ship's side. This might occur unintentionally in strong winds, when a tug is in the lee of a large ship which is drifting down upon it. Once trapped alongside it can be extremely difficult to get off again, unless the ship's speed is substantially reduced thereby relaxing the strength of the suction area. For the unfortunate tug master, this can be the start of a chain of handling difficulties which can accumulate and end in disaster.

Fig. 60(a)
Position 2

In position 2 the tug is again working in close to the ship's side and passing through an area where it is half in and half out of the respective pressure and suction zones. A positive force is pushing the bow out from the ship, while another force is pulling the stern into the ship. This combined turning couple will create a strong shear away from the ship which will require rapid and bold use of both helm and power to correct it.

Fig. 60(a)
Position 3

When working close in under the bows, in position 3, the tug may have to run slightly ahead of the ship's bow pressure zone and consequently find a very strong positive force being exerted on the stern and rudder. This will give a similar effect to that of putting the helm hard over towards the bow of the ship and the tug could sheer rapidly across its path. Bold corrective counter rudder with power will be needed instantly, but even then may be ineffective against a force which can be very strong.

Fig. 60(a)
Position 4

If the ship's speed is too high and the interaction forces correspondingly severe, or if the tug master fails to keep control, the tug can find itself in position 4 with alarming and fatal rapidity. The consequences may be flooded decks and serious collision damage, particularly from underwater contact with a ship's bulbous bow, with the possibility of capsize and loss of life. **A sudden and catastrophic loss of stability is the most likely cause of a capsize and this can occur even with a very slight collision. Tugs, it should be noted, roll over and flood extremely quickly, thus affording little time for the crew to escape!**

Interaction Aft
Fig. 60(b)

When a tug is approaching to pass a line aft it is also likely to feel the effect of interaction and may, similar to the forward tug, experience some handling difficulties. This will be particularly evident if the ship's speed has not been sufficiently reduced. The resultant interaction forces may be too strong, causing a vigorous suction, or low pressure area, around the after body of the ship (see figure 60b). This is compounded by the more obvious and widely recognised risk that is associated with working under the stern, in the close proximity of the ship's propeller.

Fig. 60(b)
Position 1
Position 2
Position 3

When a tug makes its approach and is, for example, in position 1, it will be influenced by this suction and may start to take a sheer towards the ship's stern. As this may be a low pressure area, the tug will have less water resistance ahead of it and may also experience an unexpected increase in speed. Unless quick action is taken, with counter rudder and appropriate power, the tug will be drawn unwittingly into the stern of the ship and become stuck somewhere alongside in the region of position 2. Extreme cases are possible, when the forces are so strong that the tug fails to respond to full rudder or power and may inadvertently land heavily alongside. If the ship is in ballast, partly loaded or has a large overhanging stern the tug could be drawn into position 3, with the possibility of serious structural damage to the tug's superstructure and upperworks.

The danger from the propeller is a more obvious threat and, naturally, care should be exercised whenever a tug is working close under the stern. Whilst it is 'desirable' for a conventional propeller to be stopped it is not always practicable, particularly with controllable pitch propellers, and the tug's master should always be kept fully informed as to the status of the propulsion unit when coming in close. This is, in any case, a good policy to adopt during all tug operations.

Whilst procedures vary from port to port, some tug masters may opt to make their approach in relative safety from dead astern, on the centre line of the ship. When close in, bow to stern, the first line is passed down to the tug's bow and then the tug eases out to a safer position, to complete making fast and taking up station.

Girting a Tug

There have, in the past, been serious accidents involving tugs that have resulted in a sad and tragic loss of life, and which have been caused by a phenomenon known variously as girthing, girding or girting, in differing parts of the world. With their towing hook amidships conventional tugs have always been vulnerable to girting and their basic manoeuvrability makes it all the more difficult to extricate this type of tug, should it be caught in such an unenviable position. It can be caused by one, or both of the following ......

- **the ship turning independently and too quickly away from the tug.**
- **excessive straight line speed with a tug made fast.**

Let us look at an example of a common situation, with a conventional tug forward on a long line.

Fig. 61(a)
Position 1: Forward

In this area the tug is relatively safe and regardless of whether the ship's speed is too high it does not result in any immediate problem, provided it remains within a small

Fig. 61 Girting a Conventional Tug

a) forward

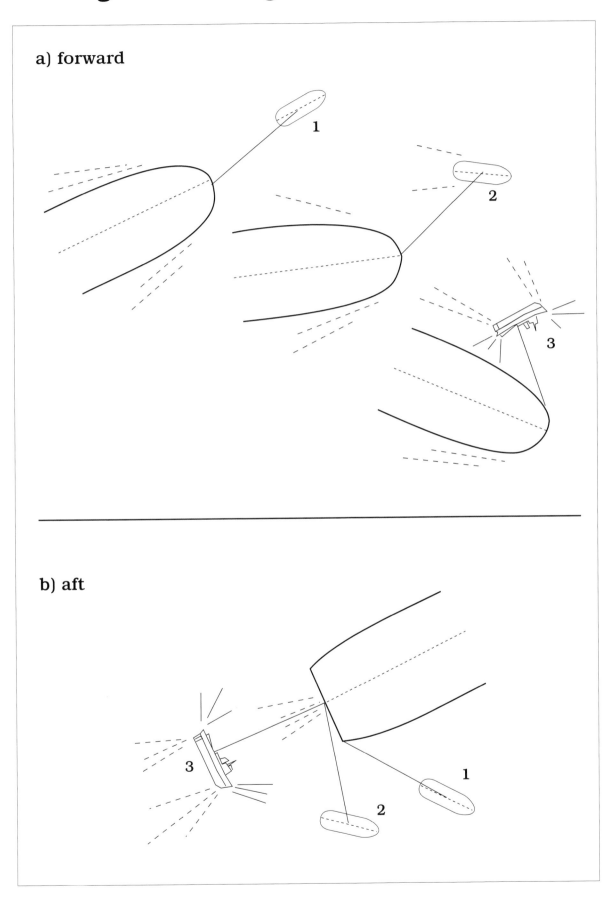

b) aft

angle on the bow. Whilst it can remain in attendance, such a small arc of relatively safe effectiveness will naturally limit its operational capabilities.

Position 2: Forward

If the tug is out in this position broad on the bow the ship could, as a result of too much starboard helm or excessive speed, or both, outrun the tug which may have neither the time nor manoeuvrability to turn and keep up with the rapidly swinging or accelerating ship.

Position 3: Forward

This is the worst possible situation where the tug is being pulled around on the radius of the tow line and because of the position of it's hook, is then dragged along with the tow line out on its beam. Due to the nature of the forces involved, it will also be pulled over to a dangerous angle of heel and unless the tow line breaks, or can be released immediately, the tug which is powerless to respond and already listing heavily, may capsize!

A conventional tug working aft, is perhaps more at risk than the forward tug, as its design characteristics frequently oblige it to lay with the tow line much more inclined towards its beam.

Fig. 61(b)
Position 1: Aft

Provided the ship is either stopped or proceeding at extremely low speeds a conventional tug can work quite efficiently with maximum bollard pull in all directions at this and any other position around the stern.

Position 2: Aft

If the ship's speed now increases, the tug will have to work around onto a heading which is more in keeping with the ship, not only to keep up with the accelerating ship but also to maintain a safe lead with the tow line. This does, however, have a tendency to encourage the tug master to work with the tow line dangerously near the tug's beam and unfortunately also results in a substantial loss of bollard pull over what was a previously large useful arc of operation.

Position 3: Aft

Should the ship's speed become excessive, or if the stern of the ship is swung rapidly away from the tug, it may be unable to respond quickly enough and could fail to keep the safe station previously illustrated. As a consequence the tug might be dragged around on the radius of the tow line to this dangerous position and capsize with shocking rapidity. It is also very important to note that a tug attending a ship aft, but in the close confines of a lock, may find itself in a similar situation, but with even less ability to manoeuvre. Should the tug get caught across the lock with a ship proceeding at too high a speed it will be exposed to a very serious risk of girting.

For those unfortunate enough to have witnessed it, a tug being girted and capsized is an awesome and frightening sight. It frequently happens too quickly to activate quick release gear and allows absolutely no time whatsoever for the evacuation of the crew who may become trapped in the submerged tug.

The Gob Rope
Fig. 62(a) and (b)

The conventional tug, in comparison with the more manoeuvrable tractor tug and azimuth stern drive tug, may be at a disadvantage as a result of ......

Fig. 62 Working a Gob Rope

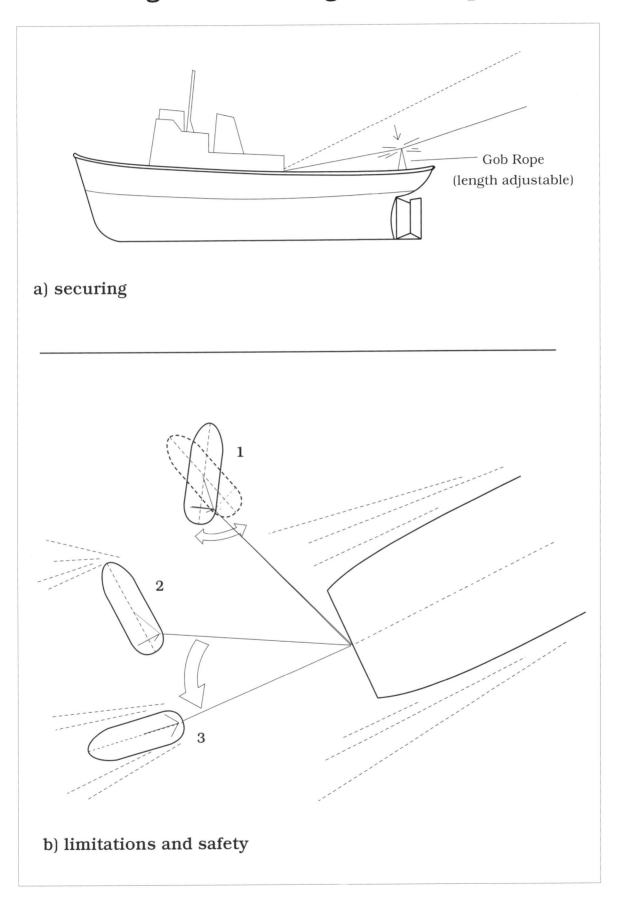

Gob Rope
(length adjustable)

a) securing

b) limitations and safety

The Gob Rope
(continued)

- **interaction**.
- **girting**.
- **excessive ship speed**.
- **confined locks and dock areas**.
- **traditional manoeuvrability**.

In certain cases, some conventional tug masters might be seen working a gob or gog rope in order to improve safety and performance (see figure 62a). This is a rope of suitable length and strength which a crew man will use on the towing deck, to bowse down or 'gob down' the main tow rope and which may subsequently be adjusted in length when required by the master. Its use brings the pivot point of the tug (see figure 59) aft to the area of the gob rope and this encourages the tug to pivot around that point and keep its stern up to the tow.

Fig. 62(b)
Position 1

Once secured, the gob rope clearly limits the manoeuvrability of the tug's stern under the tow line to a relatively small arc. On the other hand it is a good compromise as it helps to keep the tug's stern up to the ship. At suitably low speeds the tug can be usefully employed to dig in and assist when needed. The tug master may occasionally slacken the gob rope right off to regain full manoeuvrability, if it is necessary in order to reposition the tug before taking the weight again.

Fig. 62(b)
Positions 2 and 3

These two positions show the tug with it's gob rope secured, exposed to the risk of girting due to excessive ship speed and being swung around on the radius of the tow line. In this instance, however, because the gob rope has kept the pivot point aft it is being swung safely round by its stern thus giving the tug master valuable time during which the tow may be safely slipped.

Using the Tug's Weight

The conventional tug is clearly at its best when it can utilise its maximum power and apply full bollard pull to the tow line or ship when so required. Naturally, there is a tendency for this to be at its best when the ship is fairly static i.e. when swinging, positioning, breasting or lifting off, etc. To the experienced mariner these movements are by and large straight forward and do not require elaborating upon.

Forward
Fig. 63(a)

An alternative, if the bollard pull cannot be applied directly, usually because the ship is making way, is to 'lay' on the tow line and use the tug's weight to do the job, while the power is used primarily to maintain position and headway. The forward tug is illustrated doing this in figure 63a. It has eased out on the bow, all the time continuing to make headway which is comparable with the ship and is laying on the tow line using its own weight, rather than direct bollard pull alone, to swing the ship's bow to starboard. This, unfortunately, becomes increasingly less effective if the ship's speed is permitted to build up, because the tug's effort is then wasted on keeping up with the ship and maintaining a safe position.

Aft
Fig. 63(b)

In comparison to the forward tug, the after tug, if it is using its main towing hook, is much more restricted in its arc of operation. If the ship's speed is too high it is usually reduced to following the ship on a slack line until required

Fig. 63 Using the Tug's Weight

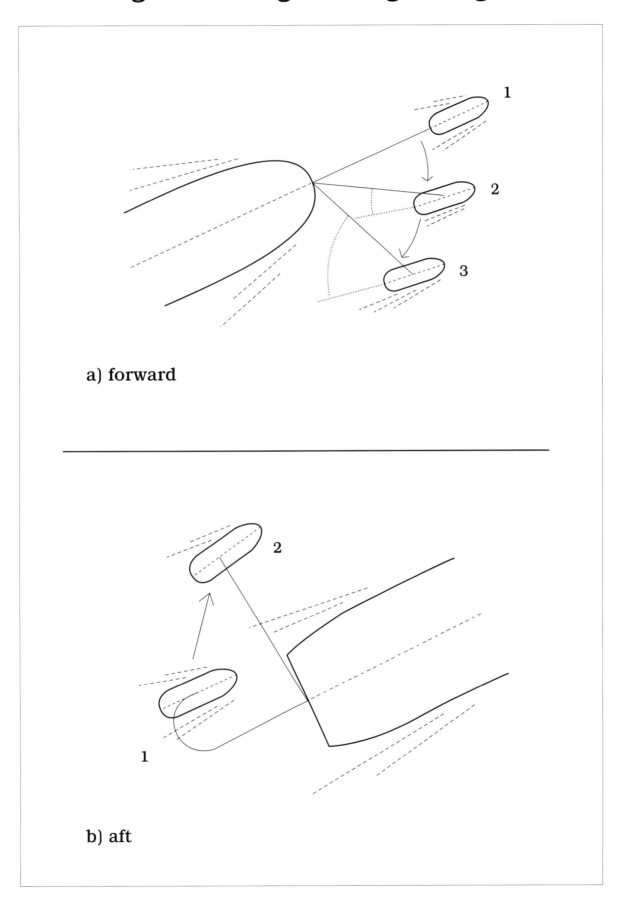

a) forward

b) aft

as shown in position 1, figure 63b. However it can, if it is safe to do so, move out to position 2 or thereabouts and 'lay' on the tow line with its own weight, but unfortunately it must keep the tow line aft of the towing hook position. Under the circumstances this design feature seriously limits the tug's arc of operation.

To overcome this limitation, a conventional tug deployed aft may occasionally be seen working with the tow line secured forward but (bearing in mind that this might then have to be let go and re-secured on the main towing hook in order to work in the conventional way) it is generally considered inconvenient and is not commonplace.

Two important things must be remembered if the tugs are being used in this way ......

- **the risk of girting is increased and the tug master must keep a close eye on the ship's speed.**

- **the tugs may impart an insidious increase in speed to the ship which needs to be monitored.**

Whilst there are clearly limitations associated with conventional tug design, it should not be forgotten that they have been the workhorse of the towage industry and are still economical, well proven and invaluable in the hands of a good tug master. They can be very powerful, modest horse power often belying excellent bollard pull, particularly by placing the propellers in shrouds or tunnels and the master can 'dig in' on a tow line and put this power to enormous effect. Manoeuvrability can also be improved by using twin propellers and bow thrusters. Notwithstanding this, however, manufacturers have developed totally different concepts in tug design in an effort to achieve outstanding tug performance and manoeuvrability.

Tractor Tugs
Fig. 64

The tractor tug represents a complete departure from the traditional design of the conventional tug, but with companies like Voith Schneider and Schottel developing tractor tugs between 1950 and 1960 it is, perhaps surprisingly, not a particularly new concept. The key to the true tractor tug lies in the use of two multi-directional propulsion units, of which some are rather like large rotating outboard motors with others consisting of rotating vertical blades. They enable the thrust units of the tug to be placed side by side, more or less under the bridge, thereby facilitating spectacular manoeuvrability in the right hands (see figure 64). Interestingly, these units have also enjoyed considerable success for many years installed on some ferries operating in inshore waters.

On a tractor tug the towing point (**P**) can be placed much nearer the stern because the propulsion units, and therefore the thrust (**T**) is always 'outside' of the towing point, thus creating a good positive turning moment (**PT**). If this is compared with the conventional tug back in figure 59 it can be seen that this is completely the opposite to the traditional configuration.

Fig. 64 Tractor Tug

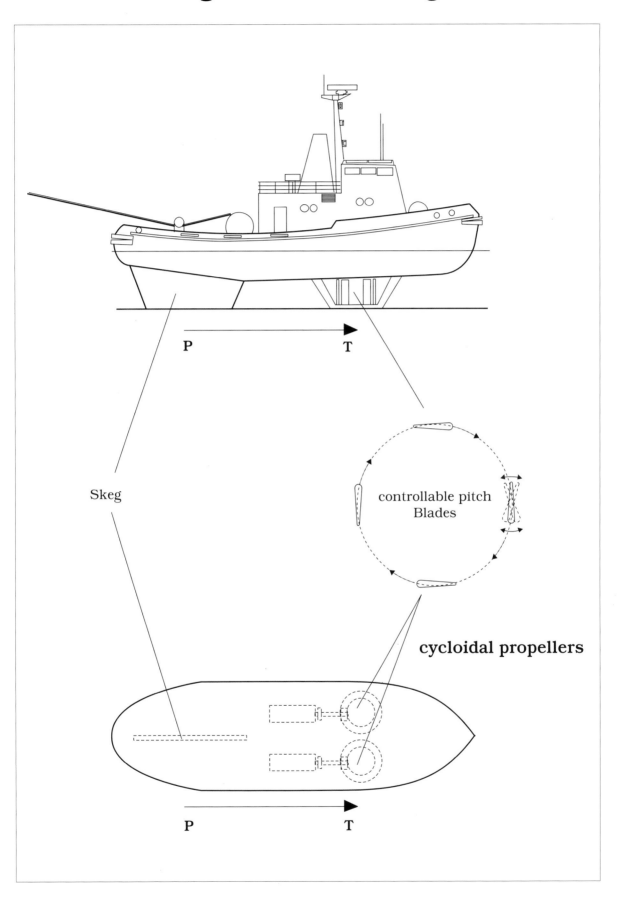

Skeg

controllable pitch
Blades

cycloidal propellers

In many cases versatility is further enhanced by working the tug's tow line directly from a winch drum with a remote control joystick control from the bridge. The tug master can thus alter the length of the tow line at will and with considerable ease (see page 48).

The tractor tug can perhaps best be defined as one where, like a farm tractor towing a trailer, the power unit is always ahead of and pulling on the towing point, unlike a conventional tug where the propulsion is actually behind the towing point and pushing it.

It may be imagined, quite correctly, when steaming at speed without a tow, that with the propulsion units thus sited this type of tug suffers from a lack of directional stability. With the power driving the tug close to the pivot point, the steering lever is indeed poor, but this is easily overcome by the versatility of the thruster units. When first learning to drive such units this initially feels a little quirky but it does not take long to get accustomed to it. Directional stability is also improved by fitting a large skeg on the centre line of the hull aft and this also supports the tug if it is dry docked or grounded.

The argument for and against tractor tugs by comparison with conventional tugs remains a matter of individual requirement being perhaps best summed up with a brief resumé. Firstly the advantages, which have to some extent already been outlined ......

Advantages of tractor tugs

- full thrust over 360 degrees.
- rapid power-on response time.
- outstanding manoeuvrability.
- able to reposition quickly if so required by the pilot.
- simple control systems.
- very low risk of girting.
- can more effectively overcome interaction forces close in on a ship.
- improved operational capability in a restricted area such as a lock or an enclosed dock.
- may decrease the 'turn round time' of port movements that normally use tug assistance.
- reliable, robust propulsion units.

It is reasonable, therefore, to view these type of tugs as extremely versatile, ideally suited to the confines of a busy harbour, river, canal or sheltered estuarial waters. There may of course be disadvantages and the following list, which is by no means exhaustive, illustrates a number of important considerations.

Disadvantages of tractor tugs

- high capital investment costs.
- less bollard pull per kilowatt power.
- repair and maintenance of complex underwater units may be expensive.
- handling in an open seaway might be poor with the short distance between the pivot point and thrust, creating a short steering lever.
- **heeling angle with full side thrust may be up to 21° with some tugs. Therefore, risk of damage can exist when laying alongside a ship**.
- sophisticated underwater units may be damaged if

Fig. 65 Azimuth Stern Drive Tug and Azimuth Propellers

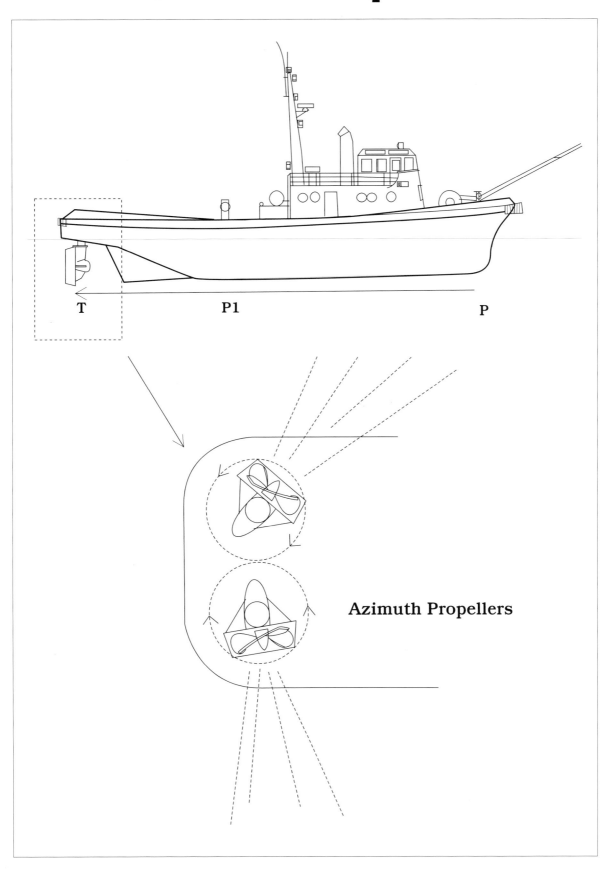

T

P1

P

Azimuth Propellers

Disadvantages of
tractor tugs
(continued)

grounded and /or fail if choked with debris.
- draft may be up to 5m, which is large in comparison to conventional tugs.
- the re-training of conventional tug masters is essential in order fully to maximise a tractor tug's potential.

Azimuth Stern Drive (ASD) Tugs
Fig. 65

There are throughout the many pilotage districts of the world, but particularly so in Japan and Australia, a substantial number of tugs known as azimuth stern or 'Z' drive tugs (see figure 65).

This tug is not, strictly speaking, a tractor tug in the true sense of the word but more of a compromise, utilising some of the benefits of both conventional and tractor tug alike. It can employ two towing positions, one amidships and one forward, and main propulsion is from two rotating azimuth units which although similar to those employed in tractor tugs are placed aft rather like a traditional twin screw tug.

The ASD tug can therefore be used in the same manner as a conventional tug, using the amidships towing position but with considerably improved handling. However, it is when using the forward towing position, usually direct from a bow towing winch, that the ASD tug realises its full potential (see page 128). With virtually the full length of the tug between the thrust units (**T**) and the forward towing point (**P**) the ASD tug can be used with great effect. It is perhaps best compared to the pure tractor tug by listing its relevant advantages and limitations.

Advantages of an ASD
Tug

- better directional stability at speed.
- more suitable hull form for open waters and working in a seaway.
- improved bollard pull per kilowatt power.
- azimuth units easy to withdraw for maintenance and repair.
- maximum heel with side thrust less than 15°.
- shallower average draft of 3m.

Limitations of an ASD
Tug

- side stepping ability not as good.
- squat at the stern and flooding of the aft deck has been known to occur with certain design types when backing with full power.
- still susceptible to girting when using the after towing position.
- slightly more at risk from the effects of interaction.
- it is not uncommon for 99% of all towing to be limited to the forward position.
- complex control systems.
- more susceptible to rubbish damage in propellers.

Combi tugs

Although not common there are some tugs in use that should, nevertheless, be mentioned, which fall into a category best described as 'combination' or 'combi' tugs. Generally speaking these are older conventional tugs that have been retrofitted with some type of thruster system forward to supplement their traditional propulsion system. This may be anything from a simple standard tunnel thruster to a sophisticated retractable azimuth thruster unit and will improve handling characteristics accordingly.

A Voith Schneider and a conventional tug in attendance

Fig. 66 Tractor Tug Forward

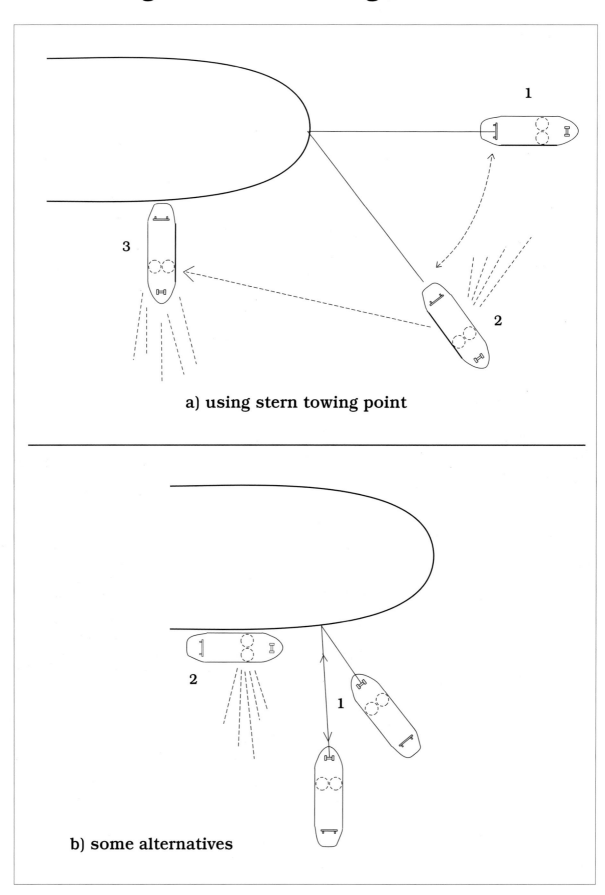

a) using stern towing point

b) some alternatives

Mixed Fleets

Many pilots will find themselves working for port authorities that are served by tug companies which are only operating substantial numbers of older, conventional tugs with perhaps, at best, just one or two modern tractor tugs. Pilots often comment that these are sometimes under utilised and that this is due mainly to the inadequate re-training of tug masters, resistance to changing methods of operation, or perhaps even a little bit of both.

This is largely historic, as it is an unfortunate fact of life that only in countries previously devastated by war and with the opportunity to rebuild stocks from scratch, or countries with strong growth industries building new ports or terminals, will you see substantial numbers of modern, powerful tractor tugs. This is, for example, particularly noticeable in Japan and some parts of Europe.

Elsewhere one can understand the dilemma of the tug operators, because it would not be an easy matter financially to update a large fleet of conventional tugs, which may still represent a comparatively recent capital investment, with costly tractor tugs that may also require new training programmes and higher maintenance budgets.

It will therefore be essential, for a long time to come, for both pilot and ship master alike to have a broad understanding of the working methods associated with both the tractor tug and the conventional tug, so that the best results can be achieved when a ship is attended by both types in a mixed fleet of tugs.

Working a tractor tug forward

Fig. 66(a)
Positions 1 and 2

In this illustration the tug is using its aft towing point and working in a similar manner to a conventional tug. Provided the ship's speed is sensibly low it can work around the radius of the tow line quickly and efficiently and thereby assist the ship with '**swinging**' or '**positioning**'. If, however, it is exposed to the risk of girting it will, unlike the conventional tug, be towed stern first in relative safety.

Position 3

If required by the pilot the tug can quickly move in and reposition alongside, shortening but retaining the tow line, particularly if it is on a remote control winch drum, to give good push-pull assistance during '**breasting**' .

Fig. 66(b)
Position 1

This shows an option whereby the tug is using a forward towing winch, if fitted, and is able adjust the length of tow as required. It may occasionally be favoured as a quick method for '**lifting off**' from a berth during departures, the tug also being able to move in to push or check the ship. It is, however, rare and not commonly practiced.

Position 2

A familiar working mode in some countries, notably America and Japan, and also elsewhere in some multi-tug operations involving large ship movements, where the tug is '**lashed up**' alongside. As previously discussed, some caution is needed by the tug in this position, as the heeling angle on full side thrust can be potentially damaging. Furthermore 'backwash and turbulence' due to the close proximity of the ship's hull will almost certainly combine to limit the full effectiveness of the tug, most predominantly when lifting off with a lot of power.

Fig. 67 Tractor Tug Aft

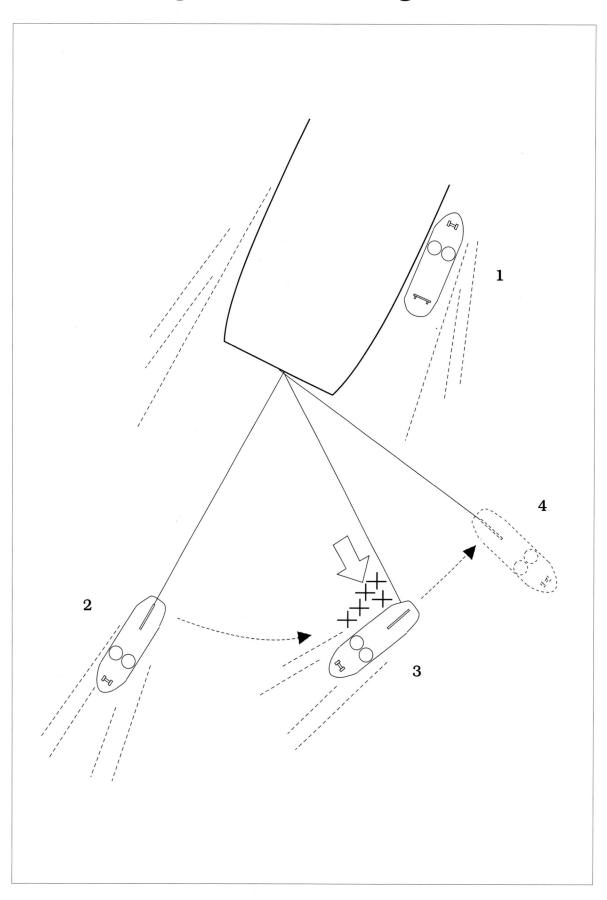

Working a tractor tug aft

Fig. 67
Position 1

This is an excellent towing position, again much favoured in Japan and the USA, and particularly good when moving 'dead ship' where the tug to some extent acts as a replacement rudder and propeller for the ship. To be reasonably effective the tug needs to be as far aft as possible, but it should be noted that the limitations associated with a tug working alongside, as mentioned in the previous example, may still apply.

Position 2

This is a working method most commonly associated with channel escort work, or any other occasion when a ship is in transit and requires tug assistance whilst making way. In this particular task the tractor tug really comes into its own and is vastly more effective than the conventional tug. The tug is secured at its aft tow point, escorting the ship stern first at reasonably modest speeds. (It is fair to say that most ASD tugs can do this as well, bow first, using their forward towing point.)

Position 3

With relatively little effort the tractor tug can ease out onto the ship's quarter to the position illustrated in this example. By putting a little tension on the tow line and using a combination of the tug's weight and water pressure it can assist the ship very effectively in swinging and steadying when it is necessary. This useful technique is known as the '**indirect towing mode**' or '**paravane effect**' and it has proven successful even when escorting very large deep draft vessels.

In the indirect towing mode, when engaged at the stern of a ship, the pull on the tow line can be increased by a factor of 1·5 to 2·0 times the bollard pull. The large underwater skeg of the tractor tug makes it particularly efficient at achieving this increased pulling power.

With its excellent manoeuvrability and inherent safety, the tractor tug aft can also readily assist the ship with slowing down or '**braking**'.

Position 4

Once the ship is subsequently either stopped, or slowed to a minimal speed, the tractor tug can work around the radius of the tow line using its excellent manoeuvrability or should it become necessary, move in quickly and reposition for work alongside.

Working an ASD tug forward

Fig. 68(a)
Position 1

Whilst there are many operational similarities to the tractor tug, the ASD tug is different by design and consequently one or two operational points should be kept in mind.

In this position the tug is, generally speaking, being used in much the same manner as a conventional tug, in that it is using its amidships towing point. Therefore although it may be very powerful and manoeuvrable, it is none the less still at risk from girting and this must, to some extent, limit its operational usefulness to that of the conventional tug.

Position 2

In comparison to the previous example, this is the more versatile operating method, with the tow connected at its bow and the thrusters ahead of the towing point, in true tractor configuration. The tug is safe in the event of girting and can side thrust effectively around the radius of the tow line. As previously mentioned, on some older design variants of this type of tug, when making way stern first, at any sort of speed with the power on, there is a tendency of the stern to be pulled down or 'squat' quite alarmingly and badly enough for the after deck to become awash and flooded. This, of course, is not acceptable and the tug master may therefore prefer, quite rightly, to revert to the conventional working method in position 1 for channel escort duties. Newer ASDs may not be susceptible to this problem.

Fig. 68(a)
Position 3

It is characteristic of this type of tug, in some areas of the world, to be designed with a conspicuously well fendered, flat nose, which facilitates either 'lashing up' or simply laying on a ship bow in. This avoids the problem of heeling angle when applying full thrust and places the thrusters further away from the ship, thus decreasing power loss through turbulence and backwash.

Some caution is needed, when tugs are approaching a ship to land bows in, as the ship's side can easily be damaged through landing too heavily!

Working an ASD tug aft
Fig. 68(b)
Position 1

If an ASD tug is attending a ship aft, it can do so in the same manner as a tractor tug by using its forward towing point and paravane out, using its own weight and water pressure to assist the ship in turning (see figure 67 position 3). It cannot, however, generate the same amount of force (through lift) as the tractor tug does with its large skeg aft.

On the completion of channel escort work, for example, when berthing or swinging, it can rapidly redeploy alongside as shown in position 2 or remain on a long line aft. This is a matter of choice for the individual pilot or ship's master and is dictated by the nature of the manoeuvre they are conducting.

Positioning a tug

In order to make the best use of a tug and achieve the desired result, it is important to position it in the right place. To do this it is necessary to ask the following questions ......

- what is the intended movement and or manoeuvre?
- will the ship be predominantly with headway, backing, or stopped?
- where will the ship's pivot point be?
- where will the tug be in relationship to the ship's pivot point?
- what type of tug is being used?

There is, therefore, given the very nature of the questions, every indication that there is a very important interactive link between the ship's pivot point and the position of the tug. This is best illustrated by looking more closely at some specific examples.

Fig. 68 Working an
Azimuth Stern Drive Tug

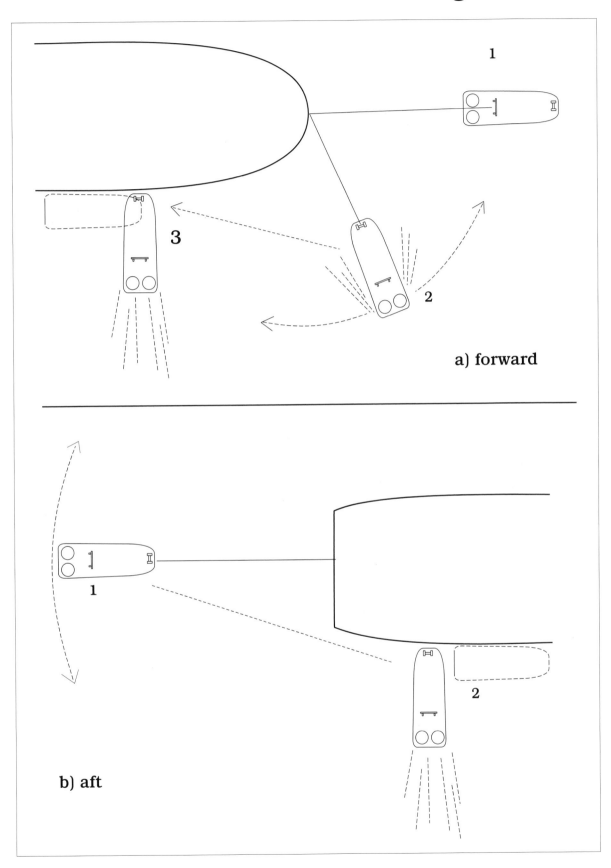

a) forward

b) aft

Fig. 69 Channel Escort

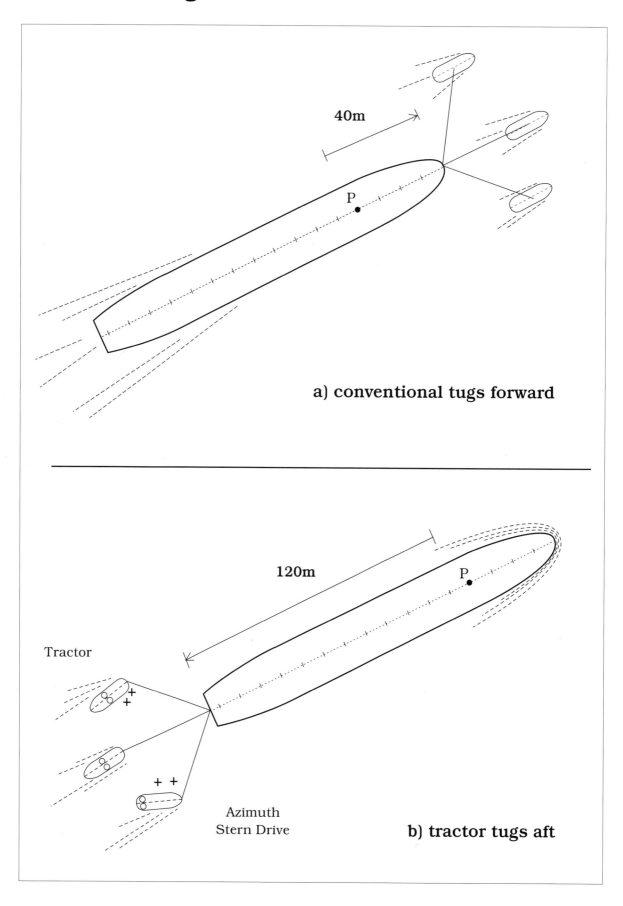

40m

P

a) conventional tugs forward

120m

P

Tractor

Azimuth
Stern Drive

b) tractor tugs aft

Channel escort tug

In very many cases when a ship is in transit of a narrow waterway it is not practicable in the interests of safety to do so without the assistance of a tug. An example of this occurs when a ship has to negotiate a bend in a channel where, due to relative ship size, shallow water, tides, wind or any combination of such restrictions, it is clearly beyond the capabilities of the ship's normal turning circles and a tug is required to improve the ship's turning ability.

Another example occurs, usually in the aftermath of a major accident and serious pollution, where legislation is passed making it mandatory to have a tug escort, even for quite long and relatively open water transits. Although the pilot and ship master may normally be quite capable of doing the job without tugs, like it or not the protection of the environment is the more important issue and the ship cannot be exposed to the threat of mechanical failure, or placed at risk from even the briefest of lapses in human judgement.

It is in the role of channel escort, that the differing operational capabilities of the tractor and conventional tug are most clearly illustrated and one where it is most difficult to break the mould of long established, traditional thinking and working methods.

Conventional tug forward
Fig. 69(a)

If only one conventional tug is to be used as an escort it is not, as discussed earlier in this section, particularly suited to working aft while the ship is making any sort of headway. This means, quite correctly, that it is usually secured forward but even then, if the speed of the ship is too high, it will be somewhat restricted in its arc of operation and effectiveness. This is further compounded by the position of the ship's pivot point which is, while it is making headway, approximately a $1/4$ of the length from forward. As a result of this the tug is working on a relatively poor turning lever. This can be illustrated, for example, with a 160 metre ship which has engaged a 20 tonne tug forward (see figure 69a). This will give an approximate turning moment of ......

40 metres x 20 tonnes = **800tm**

Tractorl tug aft
Fig. 69(b)

By comparison, if a tractor tug is engaged to escort the ship (or an ASD tug) it would, as previously illustrated, be able to work aft with considerable flexibility, due to its high manoeuvrability. Its efficiency would be even further enhanced because, unlike the example with the tug forward, it will be working on a very good turning lever of $3/4L$ of the ship (see figure 69b). Assuming for the sake of comparison that the tug is still of 20 tonne bollard pull, this will give a turning moment of ......

120 metres x 20 tonnes = **2400tm**

This is three times that of the forward turning moment and also illustrates why the effect of 'paravaning' is achieved with relatively little effort.

Braking

It is also very important to appreciate that with a tractor tug secured aft, if the ship experiences difficulties, or an emergency, which require it to slow down quickly, the tug can also dig in and act as a very effective brake, whilst still assisting to control heading.

This example clearly indicates that the position of a tug relative to the ship's pivot point strongly influences the tug's effectiveness. It is also apparent that any shift of the pivot point will also effect tug performance and this may best be illustrated with an example of tugs on long lines.

Tugs on long lines

In this example the ship is of 160 metres length with two 20 tonne bollard pull tugs in attendance, one forward and one aft, both on long lines. It is assumed for the example that the ship is on even keel, in deep water, with no wind or tide and is therefore influenced by no other obvious factors or forces.

Ship stopped
Fig. 70(a)

With the ship stopped and on even keel the centre of gravity of the ship, and pivot point, is approximately amidships. If both tugs now take the weight with full power, they will both be operating on similar turning levers of 80 m and the turning moments will be ......

Forward Tug   80m x 20t = **1600tm**
Aft Tug   80m x 20t = **1600tm**

As a result the ship will lift off, moving bodily sideways with no residual rate of turn.

Ship making headway
Fig. 70(b)

Once the ship gathers headway, even a small amount, the pivot point will move forward to a position approximately one quarter of the ship length from the bow. This substantially alters the lengths of the respective turning levers and upsets the balance between the two tugs whose turning moments will now be ......

Forward Tug   40m x 20t = **800tm**
Aft Tug   120m x 20t = **2400tm**

The tug aft is therefore considerably more efficient than the tug forward and will lift the ship's stern out much more quickly than the bow, which will appear sluggish. Alternatively this may be perceived as the ship's bow developing an undesirable swing to port.

Ship making sternway
Fig. 70(c)

If the ship, which was previously making headway, is now allowed to develop sternway, either intentionally or otherwise, the balance of the two tugs is completely changed. This is due to the shift of the ship's pivot point, from forward to a position approximately one quarter of the vessels length from the stern. The respective turning levers and turning moments are now completely altered and are as follows ......

Forward Tug   120m x 20t = **2400tm**
Aft Tug   40m x 20t = **800tm**

The tug aft, which was previously doing well, is now poor in comparison to the forward tug and the stern of the ship will appear to be sluggish when lifting off. This may also be perceived as a developing swing of the bow to starboard and opposite to the swing to port, which was experienced when the ship was making headway.

Fig. 70 Tugs on Long Lines

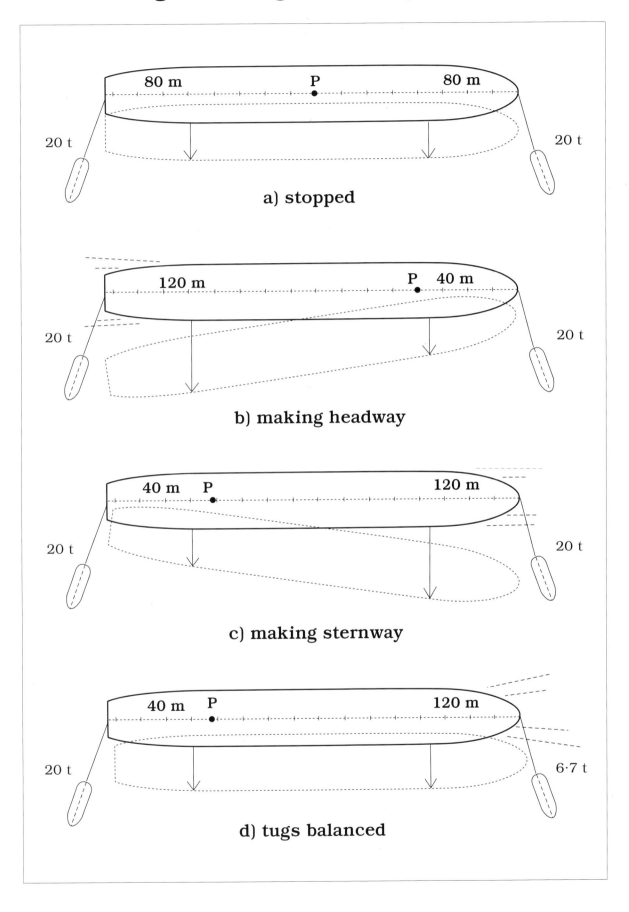

a) stopped

b) making headway

c) making sternway

d) tugs balanced

In the preceding examples with two 20 tonne bollard pull tugs the maximum lift for the ship was ......

Forward tug	**20t**
Aft Tug	**20t**
Total	**40t**

Unfortunately, if the ship is developing an undesirable swing due to headway or sternway and the tugs are at full power, it will be necessary to instruct the appropriate tug to ease back, in order to balance the tugs and correct the swing. In this particular example, with the ship making sternway, the forward tug would have to ease back to approximately one third of its potential ....

Aft tug	40m x	**20t**	= 800tm
Forward tug	120m x	**7t**	= 800tm
Totals		**27t**	Nil tm

Having ordered two tugs that appear to be quite adequate, it is very important to appreciate that there will be occasions when they will be forced to work considerably short of their full potential, particularly when compensating for an undesirable turning moment, in a situation that has already been demanding full power.

Tugs alongside

As previously mentioned in this section, some countries and some tugs, notably tractor/ASD tugs, may favour working alongside. Elsewhere it is not uncommon to employ tugs alongside, particularly when several tugs are involved in large ship movements, either to assist a ship in breasting up to a berth, or lifting off. Those countries that predominately employ tractor/ASD tugs alongside often do so most effectively. To understand this it is necessary to be aware of the interaction that exists between the tug's position alongside a ship and the position of that ships pivot point.

Ship making headway
Fig. 71(a)

When the ship is making headway, even a small amount, there is a very important difference between using a tug alongside forward, as opposed to somewhere aft. As illustrated with the ship on the left in figure 71a the forward tug is likely to be working very close to the ship's pivot point. In this position it is working on a turning lever that is either very small, or negligible and as a consequence will be relatively poor at assisting the ship to develop rate of turn or swing. However, by working close to the ship's pivot point it will be most effective in assisting the ship to develop bodily 'lateral movement', particularly when used in conjunction with full rudder and short kicks ahead by the ship.

This would, for example, be most useful when approaching a berth and it becomes necessary to press the ship in towards it, or also when lifting off during departure. With the tug being used extensively in this position, there is a considerable similarity to driving a ship with a bow thruster, but with the added advantage of much greater power over a 360° arc of operation. This also enables the pilot to use the tug for braking, or stopping the ship, with good control, if so required.

Fig. 71 Tugs Alongside

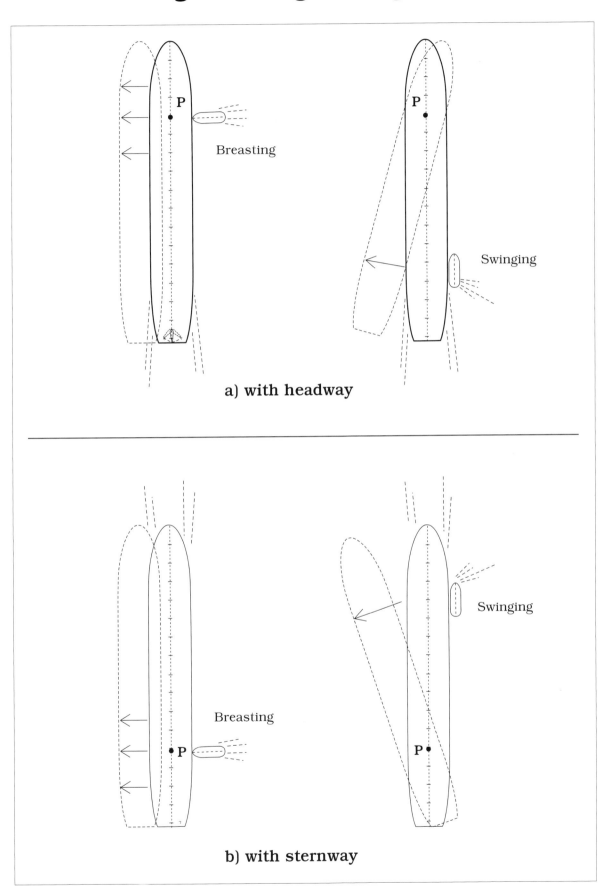

a) with headway

b) with sternway

If the tug is used aft, as depicted with the ship on the right in figure 71a, its role is very much altered. Wherever it is placed it is likely to be some distance from the ship's pivot point, working on a substantial turning lever and as such will always be best placed to help increase or decrease the ship's rate of turn, whilst making headway.

Under certain circumstances, however, this is not as successful as one would expect and may be due to the close proximity of the tug to the ship's side which creates too much backwash and turbulence for the tug to be effective, noticeably when the tug is thrusting hard away from the ship. In one port, for example, this tug is left off until a specific bend in the channel has been negotiated, before being secured for the berthing operation, which involves backing up to a berth.

Ship making sternway Fig. 71(b)

If, after having been making headway, the ship now begins to make sternway, or if the ship will be predominately making sternway, for example when backing up to a berth, it should be appreciated that the role of the two tugs previously illustrated will be reversed.

The ship's pivot point will have moved to a position approximately a quarter of the length of the ship from the stern and as shown with the ship on the left in figure 71b, the tug aft will now be actively engaged quite close to this point. In this position it is not therefore best placed to assist the ship in turning, but will be very useful in assisting the ship to develop bodily lateral motion especially when breasting in towards the berth stern first. Although perhaps, less efficient, due to its own backwash and turbulence, the tug aft will also be useful in lifting the ship 'bodily' off, typically during a stern first departure. It should still however, be borne in mind that a tug in this position is not naturally inclined towards assisting a swing, or developing a rate of turn and the outcome may therefore be quite disappointing.

Given just one tug working alongside and the need to control heading whilst making sternway, it is best placed as shown with the ship on the right in figure 71b, as far forward as practicable. In this position it is some distance from the ship's pivot point, working on a substantial turning lever and therefore able to produce a powerful turning moment when required.

It may have been noted that in some cases there exists an important correlation or similarity between tugs working alongside and a ship being worked with an operational bow thruster. This is indeed so and in many instances, if the ship is fitted with a 'good' bow thruster, it can effectively replace a tug, which might normally work alongside forward. If, on the other hand, the ship does not have a bow thruster and only one tug is available, this may perhaps be best positioned well forward in roughly the same location as a bow thruster and used accordingly.

Fig. 72 Container Ship Movement

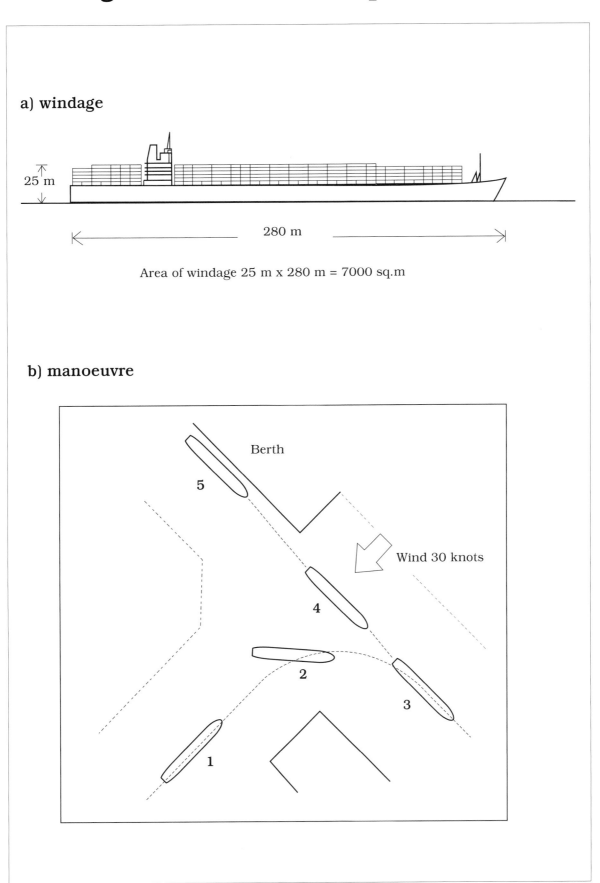

a) windage

25 m

280 m

Area of windage 25 m x 280 m = 7000 sq.m

b) manoeuvre

Berth

5

Wind 30 knots

4

2

3

1

Bollard Pull v Wind Force
Fig. 72(a)

It is important for a pilot to have a broad idea as to what wind force in tonnes is being exerted upon the ship, in comparison to the total bollard pull which is available from the local tugs. This can help, for example, in establishing the wind limits for certain vessels, or assist in analysing movements which may not be going well. With an approximate knowledge of the ship's length overall and freeboard, plus the length and height of the superstructure, including any deck cargo such as containers, it is possible to calculate roughly how many square metres of area the ship is presenting to a beam wind. The container ship in figure 72a, for example, has the following approximate overall dimensions and area of windage ......

Length	280 m
Freeboard	25 m
Total Area = (280 x 25) = **7000 sq. metres**	

Example

If we know the predicted wind speed for the intended movement it is now possible to establish a rough idea as to the force in tonnes that the ship is likely to experience.

Wind Speed = **30 knots**

Wind Speed in metres per second (V)

$$\frac{knots}{2} = \frac{30}{2} = 15 \text{ m/s}$$

Wind force in tonnes per 1000 sq.m

$$\frac{V^2}{18} = \frac{15^2}{18} = \frac{225}{18} = 12.5 \text{ t/sq.m}$$

Total Wind Force 12.5 x 7 = **88 tonnes**

(For further and more detailed reading concerning the influence of wind upon a ship please refer to chapter 5 — Effect of Wind)

To hold this ship steady with a beam wind of 30 knots would require, at the very least, a combination of tugs that offer a total bollard pull of at least 88 tonnes. However, it must also be remembered that the wind force varies as the square of the wind speed, and a gusty wind, or squall, may take the wind force well beyond that of the tugs, thereby placing considerable strain on the tug's wires. This particular ship would, for example, experience the following increases in wind force if the wind gusts to ......

- **35 knots   119 tonnes**
- **40 knots   156 tonnes**

With an approximate knowledge of the wind force and knowing the type and size of tugs to be used, it is now possible to take a closer look at a movement involving several tugs.

Multi-Tug Movement
Fig. 72(b)

In this particular example (see figure 72b) the container ship whose windage we have already established, will be inbound and intending to swing off the terminal, prior to backing up to the berth. During the manoeuvre it is anticipated that a wind of 30 knots will be blowing off the berth and also be on the ship's port beam whilst it is backing.

Available to assist the manoeuvre are the following.......

Tug 1 Forward	**40t**
Tug 2 Alongside	**30t**
Tug 3 Alongside	**40t**
Tug 4 Aft	**30t**
Thruster	**10t**

We can now look at this movement more closely, to obtain a broad idea as to whether it can be conducted safely in these particular conditions with the tugs provided. This could, for example, be very useful when discussing the movement with other interested parties such as the port authorities and may offer a more professional and substantial argument, for or against a movement, than might otherwise have been the case.

Movement 1: Discussion
Ship Stopped
Fig. 73(a)

- in the interests of simplicity, the wind in this case is shown working on the pivot point and exactly amidships thus indicating no rate of turn. It should be pointed out that in some instances, with varying ship design, it may be a little forward or aft of this position.

- tugs 1, 2 and thruster combine on their turning levers of 140, 115 and 85 respectively, forward of the pivot point, giving a total turning moment of **9300 tonnes/metre to port**.

- tugs 3 and 4 are working on turning levers of 70 and 140 metres respectively, aft of the pivot point, to give a turning lever of **7000 tonnes/metre to starboard**.

- this leaves the ship with a residual and perhaps unwanted, turning moment of 2300 tonnes/metre to port with the tugs at full power.

- to reduce this swing either tug 1, tug 2 or the thruster and maybe a combination of all three, will have to be backed off. To achieve this with tug 1, for example, it would have to pull back by nearly 25 tonnes bollard pull.

To keep the ship straight, without an undesirable swing, it will be necessary to reduce the combined potential bollard pull of 150t to 125t. Fortunately this should still cope reasonably well with the 88 tonnes of wind force without compromising the manoeuvre.

Making Sternway
Fig. 73(b)

Once the ship begins to back up, the pivot point moves aft and affects the balance of the tugs quite seriously.

Fig. 73 Movement 1. Discussion

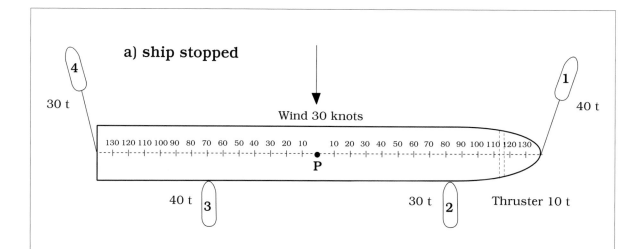

a) ship stopped

Wind 30 knots

130 120 110 100 90 80 70 60 50 40 30 20 10   10 20 30 40 50 60 70 80 90 100 110 120 130

P

40 t
30 t
40 t
30 t
Thruster 10 t

	Force in Tonnes		Levers in Metres		Turning Moments	
	Port	Starboard	Forward	Aft	Port	Starboard
Wind		88				
Tug 1	40		140		5600	
Thruster	10		115		1150	
Tug 2	30		85		2550	
Tug 3	40			70		2800
Tug 4	30			140		4200
Totals	150	88			9300	7000

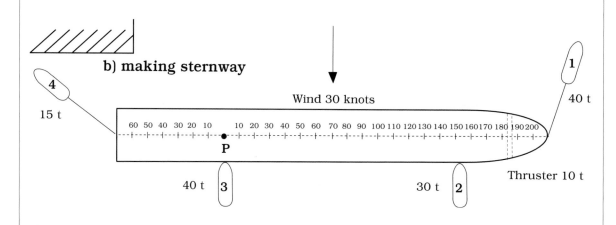

b) making sternway

Wind 30 knots

60 50 40 30 20 10   10 20 30 40 50 60 70 80 90 100 110 120 130 140 150 160 170 180 190 200

P

15 t
40 t
40 t
30 t
Thruster 10 t

	Force in Tonnes		Levers in Metres		Turning Moments	
	Port	Starboard	Forward	Aft	Port	Starboard
Wind		88	70			6160
Tug 1	40		210		8400	
Thruster	10		185		1850	
Tug 2	30		155		4650	
Tug 3	40					
Tug 4	15			70		1050
Totals	135	88			14900	7210

Fig. 74 Movement 2. Discussion

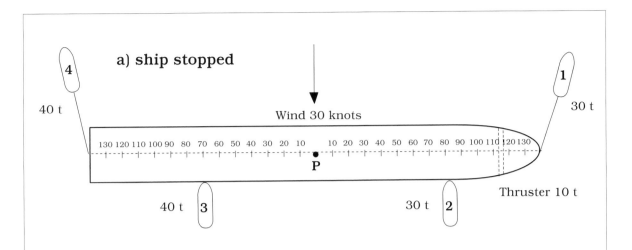

a) ship stopped

Wind 30 knots

40 t ... 30 t

Thruster 10 t

40 t 3 ... 30 t 2

	Force in Tonnes		Levers in Metres		Turning Moments	
	Port	Starboard	Forward	Aft	Port	Starboard
Wind		88				
Tug 1	30		140		4200	
Thruster	10		115		1150	
Tug 2	30		85		2250	
Tug 3	40			70		2800
Tug 4	40			140		5600
Totals	150	88			7900	8400

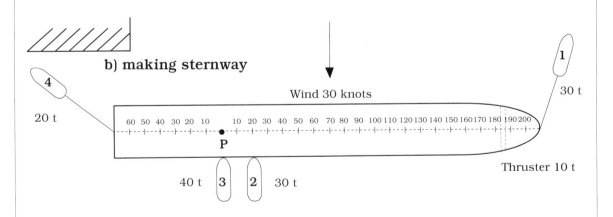

b) making sternway

Wind 30 knots

20 t

Thruster 10 t

40 t 3 2 30 t

	Force in Tonnes		Levers in Metres		Turning Moments	
	Port	Starboard	Forward	Aft	Port	Starboard
Wind		88	70			6160
Tug 1	30		210		6300	
Thruster	10		185		1850	
Tug 2	30		20		600	
Tug 3	40					
Tug 4	20			70		1400
Totals	130	88			8750	8160

- with the pivot point now further aft the wind force of 88 tonnes is now able to get to work on a 70 metre lever, producing a **6160 tonnes/metre turning moment to starboard**.

- tugs 1 and 2 and the thruster are now working on excellent turning levers of 210, 185 and 155 metres respectively, thus giving a combined and very large turning moment of **14,900 tonnes/metre to port**.

- tug 3 is now positioned either on, or at least close to, the pivot point and is therefore able to exert full power without incurring any turning moment.

- the aft tug 4 is now shown with an arbitrary reduction in bollard pull to 15 tonnes, as it approaches the restrictive close proximity of the dock side. This coupled with a turning lever that is now reduced to 70 metres, results in a poor turning moment of 1,050 tonnes/metre to starboard which is very poor.

- **the residual of these various turning moments is a very substantial 7,690 tonnes/metre resulting in the stern swinging to starboard, down wind and away from the berth**.

- to stop this swing either tug 1, tug 2, the thruster, or a combination of all three, will need to be backed off. Tug 1, for example, could be stopped altogether which would result in a loss of 40 tonnes of bollard pull. This brings the combined potential bollard pull, with all the tugs 'digging in full' down to 110 tonnes, thus leaving an almost certainly unacceptable margin of safety against the 88t of wind force.

This clearly highlights the dilemma of some tug operations, wherein the total bollard pull appears substantial in the first instance, but is seriously reduced by the need to control an unexpected rate of turn, simply as a result of commencing to make sternway, or indeed headway. This can also place a tug under sudden and unexpected loads, which can easily break a tow line. It is perhaps worth looking to see if the tugs can be repositioned to better effect?

Movement 2: Discussion

The crucial thing in this operation is to get more power aft of the pivot point, in order to counterbalance the excessive swing of the stern away from its desired track when backing, but without compromising the availability of full power should it be required. Some small changes in tug positioning could perhaps help.

Ship Stopped
Fig. 74(a)

- because the after tug is working at such a disadvantage on a poor turning lever, we can help by exchanging it with the more powerful 40t forward tug. If this were a tractor tug there might also be less loss of power, when hampered by the closeness of the berth and it may also be quite useful aft, during the channel approach phase.

Making Sternway
Fig. 74(b)

- this has reduced much of the previous imbalance and the residual turning moment of 500 tonnes/metre to starboard, is tolerable and easily adjusted.

- by the time the ship commences to make sternway, tug 2 might be repositioned aft, as close to the pivot point as practicable and adjacent to tug 3, where they can both work on full power, without creating excessive turning moments. Given its ability to reposition quickly when so required, this task might best be given to a tractor tug.

- in the interest of a safety margin tug 4 is still assumed to experience a loss of effectiveness to 20t as it closes the berth.

- **the turning moments are now very well balanced with a small insignificant residual turning moment of 590 tonnes/metre to port**.

- all four tugs can 'dig in' with full power and press the ship up without inducing excessive swing.

This particular movement has been picked at random to illustrate how an approximate, but useful, assessment can be made of any manoeuvre involving the positioning of tugs, and then be rethought or adjusted to improve the overall situation. It is also possible that such an analysis, no matter how simple, may indicate in advance that a particular manoeuvre is unlikely to work! The importance of this exercise also demonstrates the need for planning and prior information of available tugs.

For further reading on this subject please consult *Tug Use in Port* by H Hensen (see endpiece).

Conclusion

As with all shiphandling, the arguments and suggestions in this example are by no means exhaustive or conclusive and may well generate and encourage further ideas for discussion.

It is perhaps worth remembering a few words from the beginning of this section ......

"Given such a wide sphere of operations across the world, it is obviously difficult to develop general instructional material for tug operations. Not surprisingly, in some cases, it may come into conflict with more specific individual working methods. These naturally take priority and this is fully appreciated and understood."

With this in mind it is hoped that the overall objective of this section, "to offer a broad overview of the use of tugs in ship handling", will be especially useful to those new to tug operations. It will also be useful to the more experienced ship handler when occasionally, for a variety of professional reasons, it becomes necessary to analyse a movement in more depth.

In conclusion the aim of this book has been to improve shiphandling safety by illustrating the factors which need to be understood in order to keep movements under control. The necessary knowledge and skills have to be acquired by all involved in shiphandling so that manoeuvres can be planned, monitored and adjusted. Shiphandling is teamwork and all members of the team should share a common understanding of the principles involved.

To improve techniques it is essential to be able to discuss evolutions and their consequences. If this book achieves this end it will have served its purpose.

INDEX

REFERENCES

The Behaviour and Handling of Ships   Henry H. Hooyer FNI
                                             Cornell Maritime Press

Harbour Pilotage   R.A.B. Ardley
                                             Faber and Faber

Film 'Ship Handling 1' — Turning   British Maritime Technology
Film 'Ship Handling 2' — Slow and Stop   British Maritime Technology
Film 'Interaction'   British Maritime Technology

Manoeuvring single screw vessels fitted
with controllable pitch propellers in   H. Hensen FNI
confined waters   The Nautical Institute

Anchoring Systems and Procedures   Oil Companies
for Large Tankers   International Marine Forum

Prediction of Wind and Current Loads on VLCCs Oil Companies
                                             International Marine Forum

Practical Ship Handling   Malcolm C. Armstrong FNI
                                             Brown Son and Ferguson

Manned Model Ship Handling Courses   Warsash Maritime Centre
Ship Simulator Courses   Southampton, England

Manoeuvring Information for the Pilot and Navigator Thomas G. Knierim
Its source value and limitations   Sandy Hook Pilot 1991
                                             Society of Naval Architects
                                             and Marine Engineers, U.S.A

The Nautical Institute on Pilotage and Shiphandling The Nautical Institute

Video: Shiphandling with Tractor Tugs   H. Hederstrom FNI
                                             Gothenburg Port

THE NAUTICAL INSTITUTE

Navigational control training book series

The safe and timely arrival and departure of ships implies a well structured nautical organisation based upon a knowledge of proven principles and the application of effective working practices.

Hitherto shiphandling, pilotage, passage planning and watchkeeping have been considered as separate activities and in many situations it has become quite common to handover the control of the ship to the pilot without monitoring progress.

The Nautical Institute's Council maintains that teamwork is essential in the navigation of a vessel. Masters, watchkeeping officers and pilots must have an understanding of the principles involved and an organisation in place appropriate to the expected risks.

The four books covering navigational control, the *The Shiphandler's Guide; Bridge Team Management, Bridge Watchkeeping* and *Tug Use in Port*, now provide comprehensive coverage for an effective nautical response and they should be used in companies, training establishments and by individuals.

The other books in the series are:

Bridge Team Management
by Captain A.J. Swift FNI

This covers Team management; Error chains; Casualties and causes; Groundings and causes; Bridge organisation; Passage appraisal; Passage Planning; Situational awareness; Executing the plan; Monitoring the ship's progress; Navigating with a pilot on board; Automatic bridge systems, plus useful annexes.

Bridge Watchkeeping
A practical guide

Designed as a self study training guide this book examines, Preparing for sea; Watchkeeping in pilotage waters; Pilot boarding and discharge; Watchkeeping in coastal waters; Making a landfall; Anchoring and anchor watches; Watchkeeping in reduced visibility; Taking over the watch; Calling the master; Responding to emergencies; Error management; Collision Avoidance; Record keeping; Automated bridges. This book has a comprehensive set of annexes which include the Regulations for Preventing Collisions at Sea.

Tug Use in Port
by Captain H. Hensen FNI

This practical guide examines the development of harbour and escort tugs and describes how they are used for shiphandling. The foundation of the book is a questionnaire to port authorities around the world: so providing a comprehensive overview of tug working methods. The author is a retired Rotterdam pilot and includes diagrams and text to illustrate in a practical way how to use tugs effectively. Safety, training and operations are also covered, making this book an essential reference work for harbour authorities, pilots, tugmasters and sea staff.

All books are available from —
The Nautical Institute, 202 Lambeth Road, London SEI 7LQ, Fax 0207 401 2817.